11+ Non-Verbal Reasoning
3D & Spatial

For the CEM test

3D & Spatial questions are a seriously tricky part of the CEM 11+, so we've made a whole book of 10-Minute Tests to help children master them!

Each test is packed with realistic CEM-style questions, with detailed answers included in a pull-out booklet. There's even a progress chart to keep track of children's scores.

This is Book 1. You'll find more practice at the same difficulty level in Book 2!

10-Minute Tests

Ages
10-11

How to use this book

This book is made up of 10-minute tests and puzzle pages.
There are answers and detailed explanations in the pull-out section at the back of the book.

10-Minute Tests

* There are 31 tests in this book, each containing 17 or 18 questions.

* Each test is designed to focus on 3D and spatial questions that your child could come across in their 11+ test. They cover a variety of skills and techniques at the right difficulty levels.

* Your child should aim to score at least 15 in each 10-minute test.
  If they score less than this, use their results to work out the areas they need more practice on.

* If your child hasn't managed to finish the test in time, they need to work on increasing their speed, whereas if they have made a lot of mistakes, they need to work more carefully.

* Keep track of your child's scores using the progress chart on the inside back cover of the book.

Puzzle Pages

* There are 10 puzzle pages in this book, which are a great break from test-style questions. They encourage children to practise the same skills that they will need in the test, but in a fun way.

Published by CGP

Editors:
Joanna Daniels, Alex Fairer, Ceara Hayden, Catherine Heygate, David Maliphant, Andy Park and Ben Train.

With thanks to Alison Griffin and Sharon Keeley-Holden for the proofreading.

Please note that CGP is not associated with CEM or The University of Durham in any way.
This book does not include any official questions and it is not endorsed by CEM or The University of Durham.
CEM, Centre for Evaluation and Monitoring, Durham University and *The University of Durham*
are all trademarks of The University of Durham.

ISBN: 978 1 78908 196 1
Printed by Elanders Ltd, Newcastle upon Tyne
Clipart from Corel®

Based on the classic CGP style created by Richard Parsons.

Contents

Question Type Examples

These pages contain a completed example question for each question type that appears in this book. Have a look through them to familiarise yourself with the question types before you do the tests.

Building Blocks

Work out which set of blocks can be put together to make the 3D figure on the left.

Example:

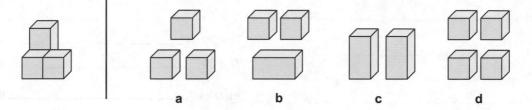

a   b   c   d

Answer: b

The block at the bottom of B rotates to become the block at the back of the figure. The two cubes move to the front.

Complete the Shape

Without rotating the figure on the left, work out which option fits onto it to make the 3D shape in the grey box.

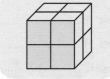

Example:

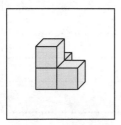   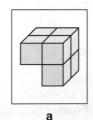   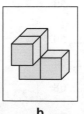   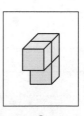   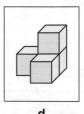

a   b   c   d

Answer: d

D rotates 90 degrees anticlockwise in the plane of the page (see the glossary on page 142) to fit with the figure on the left.

3D Rotation

Work out which 3D figure in the grey box has been rotated to make the new 3D figure.

Example:

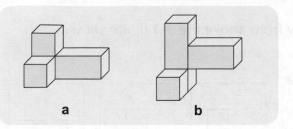 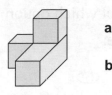

Answer: a

Figure A has been rotated 90 degrees right-to-left (see the glossary on page 142).

Fold along the Line

Work out which option shows the figure on the left when folded along the dotted line.

Example:

a   b   c   d

Answer: a

The small triangle above the dotted line folds down.

Fold and Punch

A square is folded and then a hole is punched, as shown on the left.
Work out which option shows the square when unfolded.

Example:

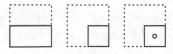

a   b   c   d

Answer: c

For the 2D Views of 3D Shapes questions, you could be asked to pick out the view from the **left**, **right**, **back** or from **above** the 3D figure. Make sure you read the question carefully.

2D Views of 3D Shapes

Work out which option is a 2D view from **above** the 3D figure shown.

Example:

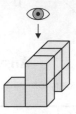 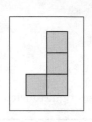 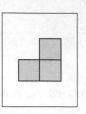 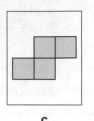 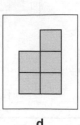

   a   b   c   d

Answer: a

There are four blocks visible from above, which rules out B and D.
There is a line of three blocks on the right-hand side of the shape, which rules out C.

Work out which option is a 2D view from the **left** of the 3D figure shown.

Example:

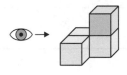 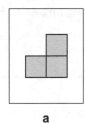 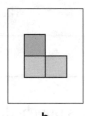 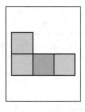 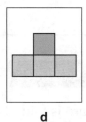

   a   b   c   d

Answer: b

There are three blocks visible from the left, which rules out C and D.
There is a blue block at the top of the figure, which rules out A.

For the Different Views of 3D Shapes questions, you could be asked to find the view from the **left**, **right**, **back** or from **above** the 3D figure. Make sure you read the question carefully.

Work out which option is the 3D figure viewed from the **right**.

Example:

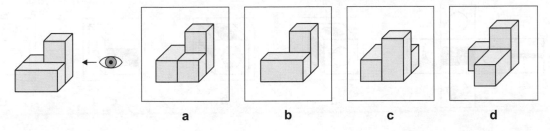

a   b   c   d

Answer: c

There is a vertical block two cubes high visible at the front when viewed from the right, which rules out A, B and D.

Work out which option is the 3D figure viewed from the **back**.

Example:

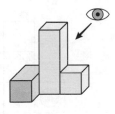 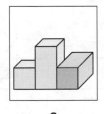 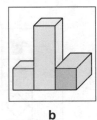 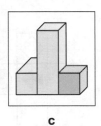 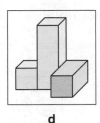

a   b   c   d

Answer: b

In option A, the middle block is the wrong size. The cube is grey, which rules out C. When viewed from the back, the blue block should go away from you, which rules out D.

For questions involving nets, the net must be folded **into** the page —
see the glossary on page 142.

Cubes and Nets

Work out which of the four cubes can be made from the net.

Example:

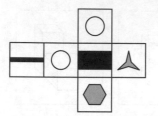

a   b   c   d

Answer: c

There is no black circle, which rules out A. The thick black line and the thin black line must be on opposite sides, which rules out B. There is only one grey hexagon, which rules out D.

Partial Nets

Work out which of the four partial nets can be folded to make the cube on the left.

Example:

 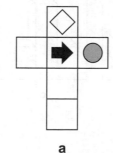 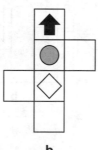 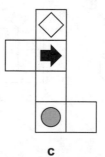 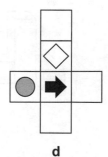

a   b   c   d

Answer: d

The arrow points away from the circle, which rules out A.
None of the shapes can be on opposite sides, which rules out B and C.

Shaded Nets

Work out which of the 3D shapes can be made from the net.

Example:

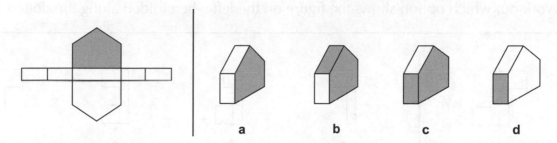

a   b   c   d

Answer: a

In the net, all the rectangular faces are white, which rules out B, C and D.

Cube Views

The figures on the left show different views of the same cube. All the cube faces are different. Work out which of the options should replace the blue cube face.

Example:

a   b   c   d

Answer: b

In the first two figures, the grey triangle points to the white heart.
So in the third figure, the grey triangle must also point to the white heart.

You have **10 minutes** to do this test. Circle the letter for each correct answer.

> Work out which option shows the figure on the left when folded along the dotted line.

1.

a   b   c   d

2.

a   b   c   d

3.

a   b   c   d

4.

a   b   c   d

5.

 a   b   c   d

Work out which option is the 3D figure viewed from **above**.

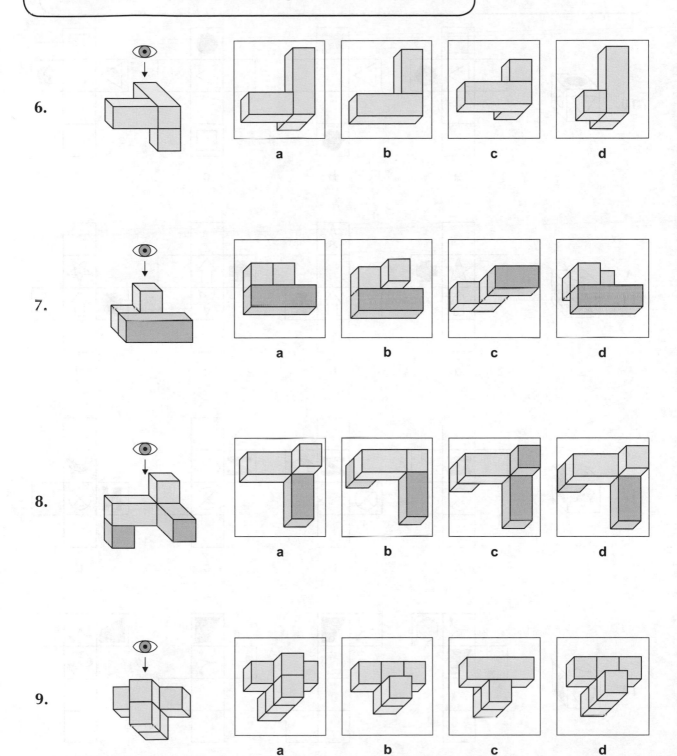

6.

a   b   c   d

7.

a   b   c   d

8.

a   b   c   d

9.

a   b   c   d

9

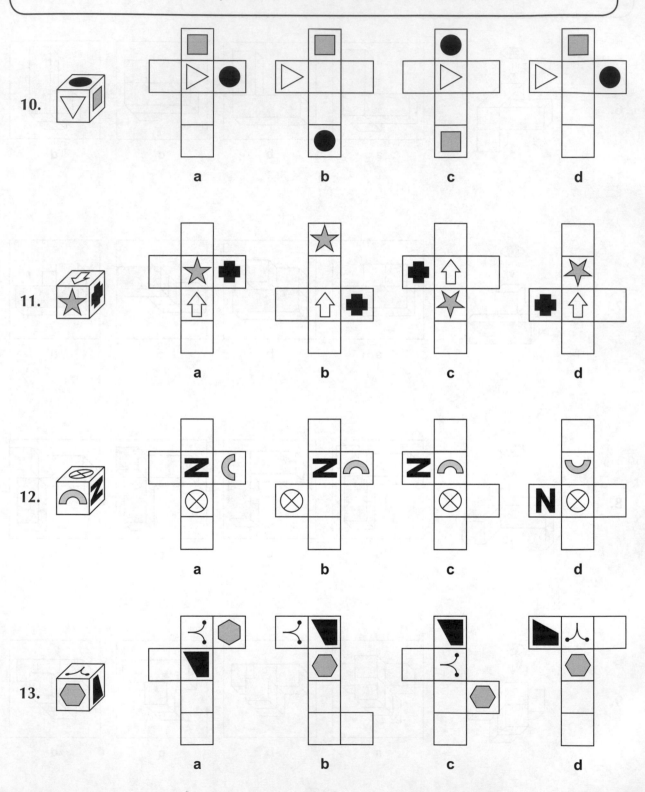

10.

a

b

c

d

11.

a

b

c

d

12.

a

b

c

d

13.

a

b

c

d

10

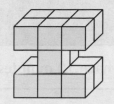

14.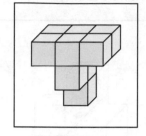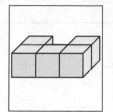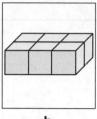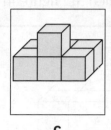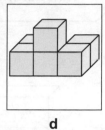

a   b   c   d

15.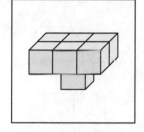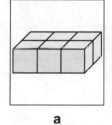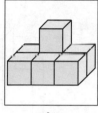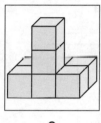

a   b   c   d

16.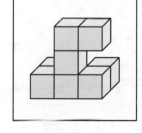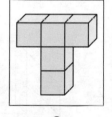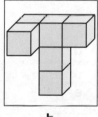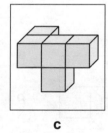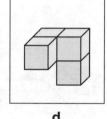

a   b   c   d

17.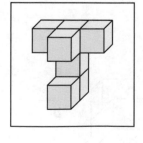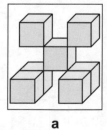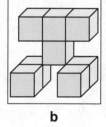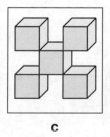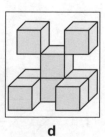

a   b   c   d

/ 17

Test 2

You have **10 minutes** to do this test. Circle the letter for each correct answer.

> Work out which 3D figure in the grey box has been rotated to make the new 3D figure.

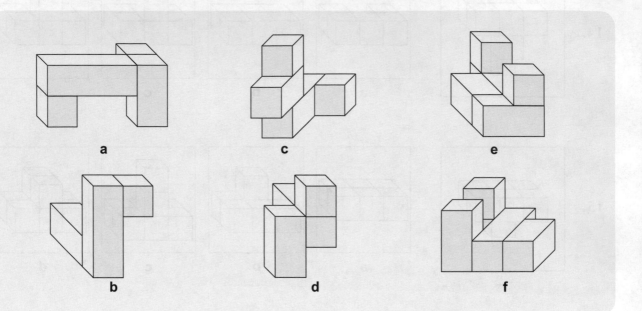

a

c

e

b

d

f

1.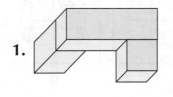

a	d
b	e
c	f

2.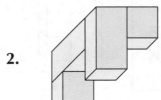

a	d
b	e
c	f

3.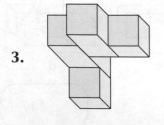

a	d
b	e
c	f

4.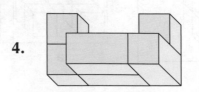

a	d
b	e
c	f

Work out which of the four cubes can be made from the net.

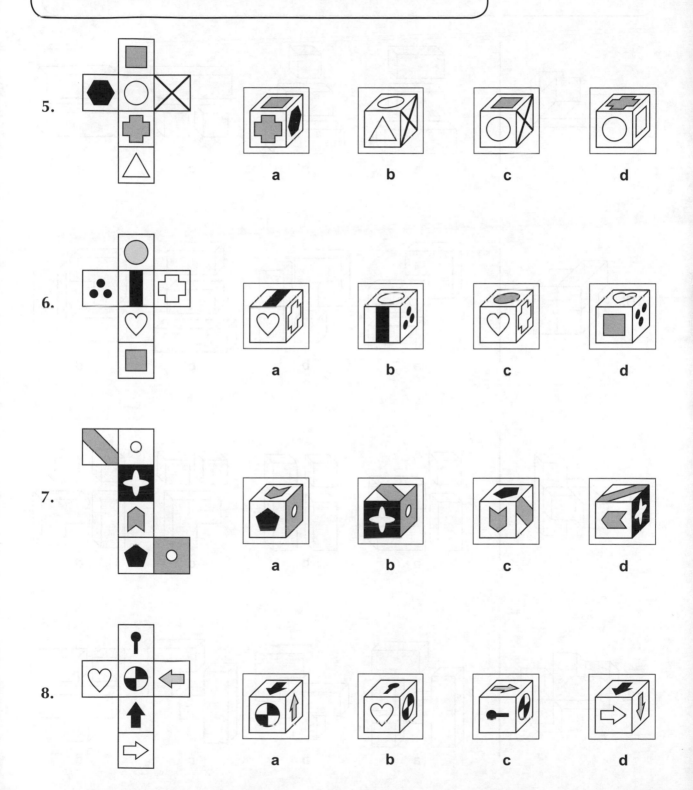

5.

    a   b   c   d

6.

    a   b   c   d

7.

    a   b   c   d

8.

    a   b   c   d

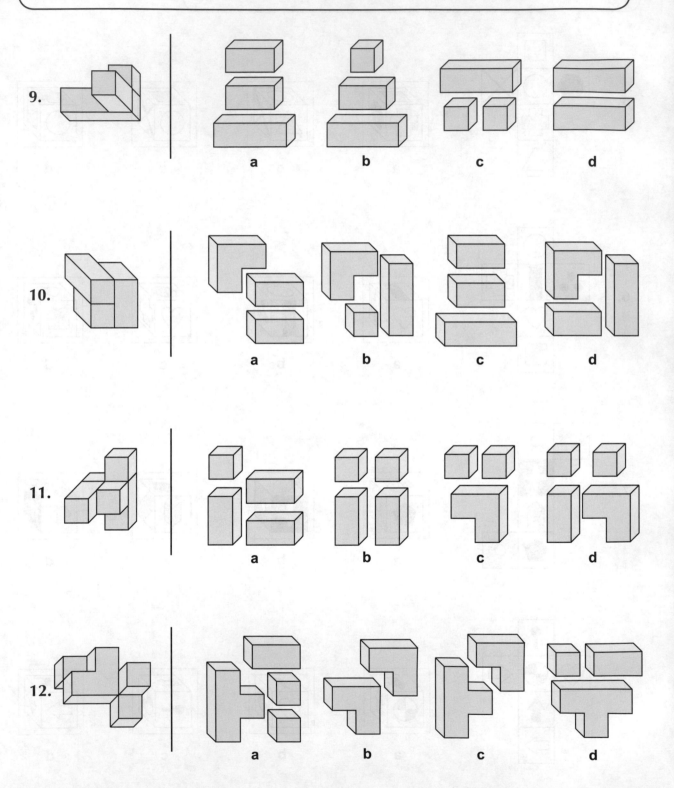

9.

a   b   c   d

10.

a   b   c   d

11.

a   b   c   d

12.

a   b   c   d

14

A square is folded and then a hole is punched, as shown on the left.
Work out which option shows the square when unfolded.

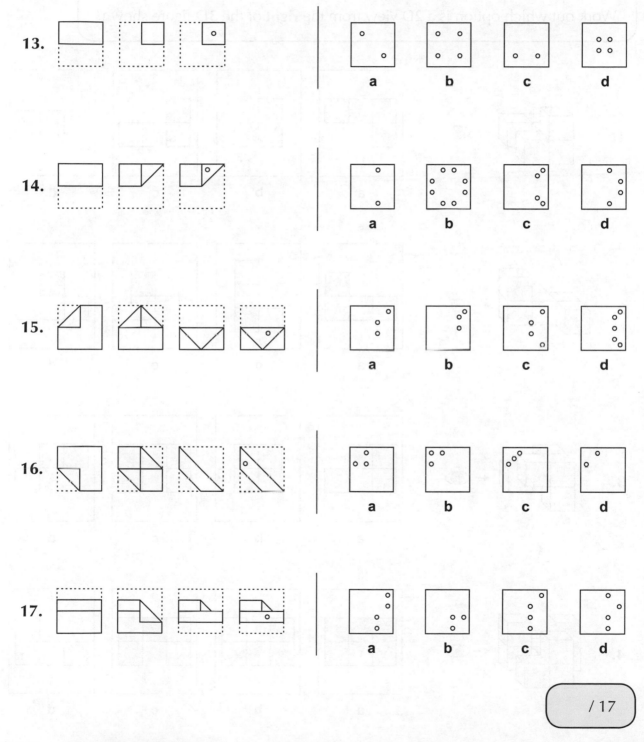

13.

a   b   c   d

14.

a   b   c   d

15.

a   b   c   d

16.

a   b   c   d

17.

a   b   c   d

/ 17

15

You have **10 minutes** to do this test. Circle the letter for each correct answer.

Work out which option is a 2D view from the **right** of the 3D figure shown.

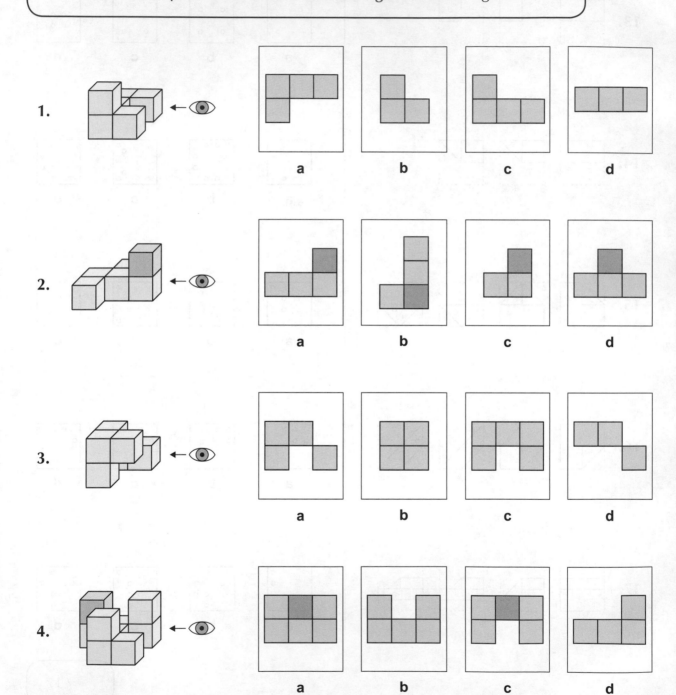

1.

a   b   c   d

2.

a   b   c   d

3.

a   b   c   d

4.

a   b   c   d

Work out which of the 3D shapes can be made from the net.

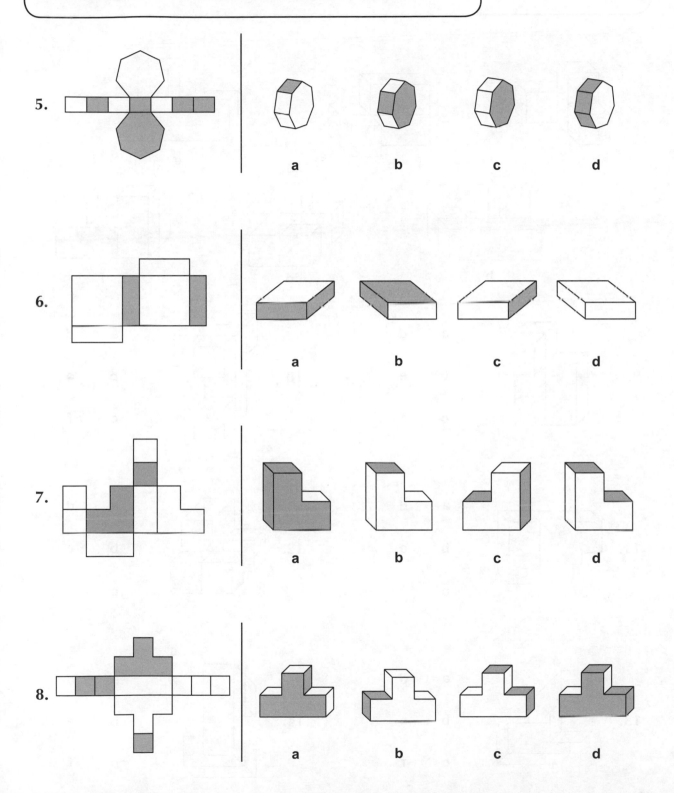

5.

a   b   c   d

6.

a   b   c   d

7.

a   b   c   d

8.

a   b   c   d

17

Work out which 3D figure in the grey box has been rotated to make the new 3D figure.

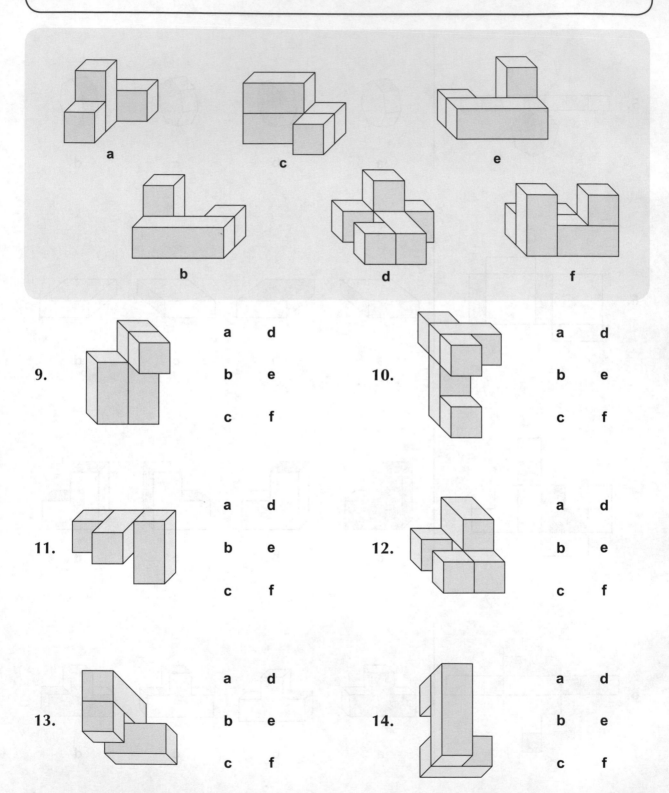

9.
a   d
b   e
c   f

10.
a   d
b   e
c   f

11.
a   d
b   e
c   f

12.
a   d
b   e
c   f

13.
a   d
b   e
c   f

14.
a   d
b   e
c   f

The figures on the left show different views of the same cube. All the cube faces are different. Work out which of the options should replace the blue cube face.

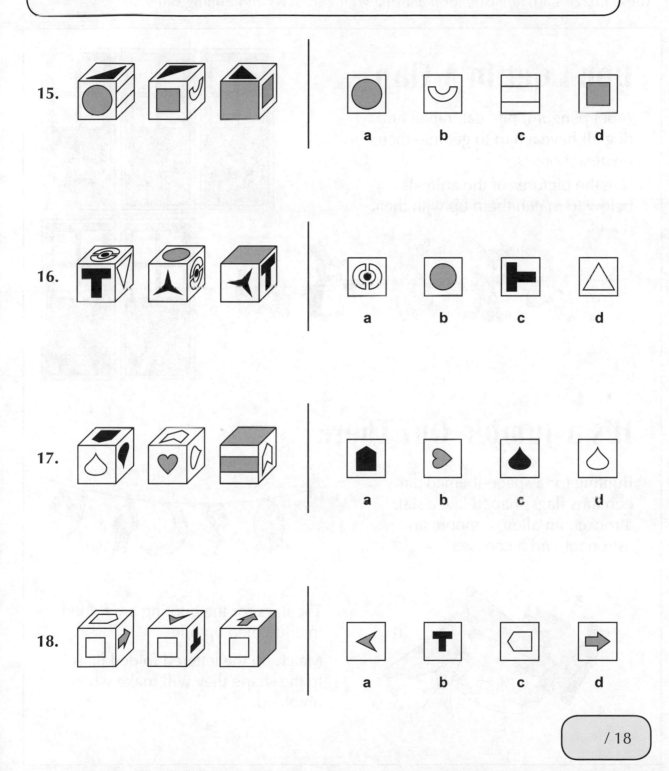

15.

a   b   c   d

16.

a   b   c   d

17.

a   b   c   d

18.

a   b   c   d

/ 18

Test 3

These puzzles are fantastic for practising your **2D-views** and **folding** skills...

Don't Get In A Flap

A pet penguin, pig, cat, rabbit and dog all have a flap to get into their owners' houses.

Use the pictures of the animals below to match them up with their doors.

It's a Jumble Out There

Bunting for a space-themed party contains flags shaped like a star, a rocket, an alien, a moon, an astronaut and a cheese.

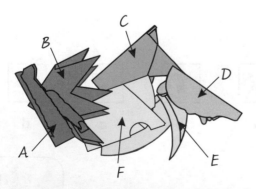

The flags for the bunting are folded in a jumbled up pile.

Match up the lettered folded flags to the shape they will make when unfolded.

20

You have **10 minutes** to do this test. Circle the letter for each correct answer.

Work out which option is the 3D figure viewed from the **right**.

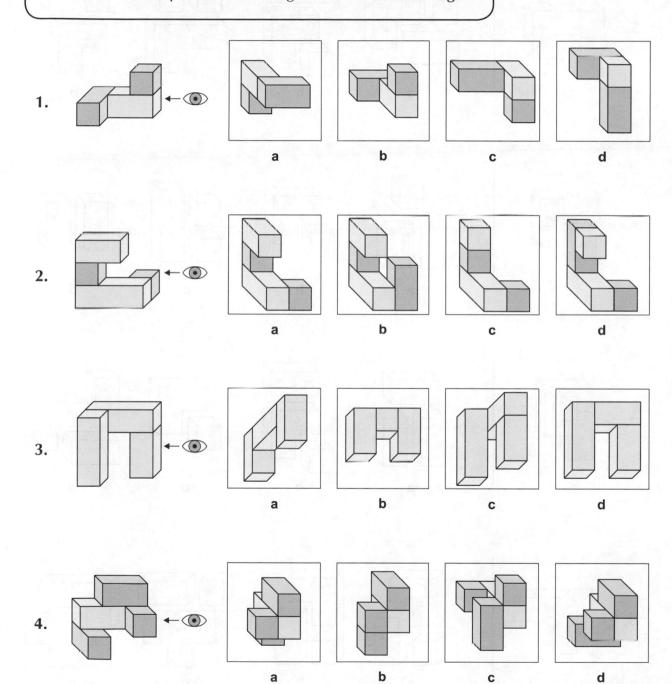

1.

    a   b   c   d

2.

    a   b   c   d

3.

    a   b   c   d

4.

    a   b   c   d

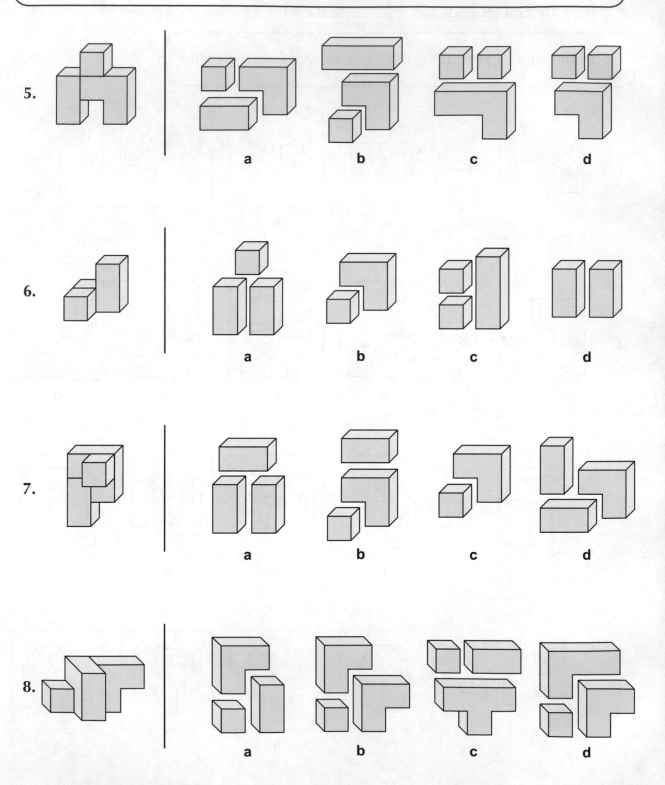

5.

a b c d

6.

a b c d

7.

a b c d

8.

a b c d

22

Work out which option shows the figure on the left when folded along the dotted line.

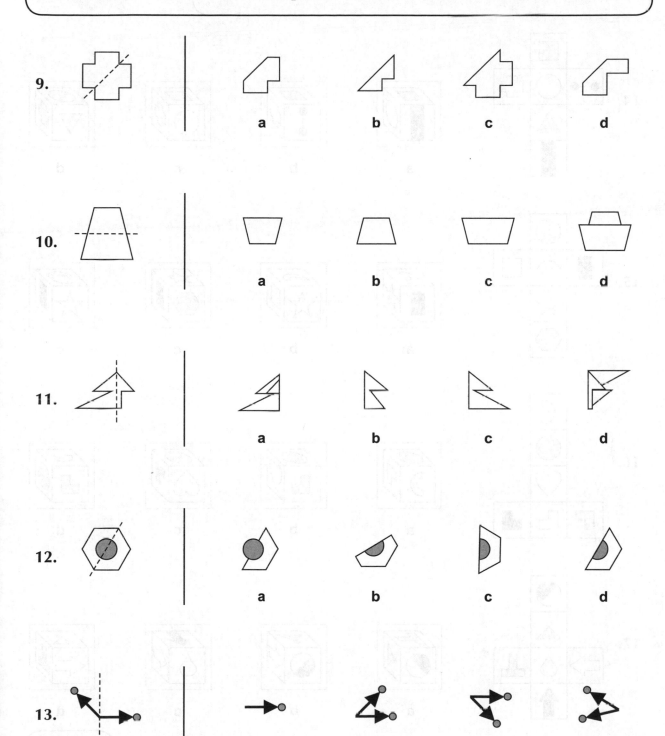

9.

a   b   c   d

10.

a   b   c   d

11.

a   b   c   d

12.

a   b   c   d

13.

a   b   c   d

23

Work out which of the four cubes can be made from the net.

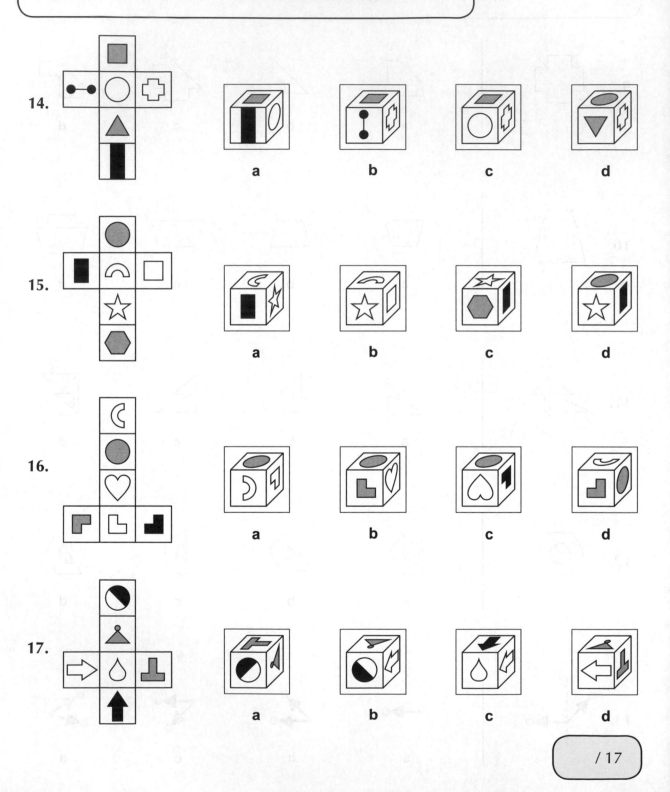

14.

a   b   c   d

15.

a   b   c   d

16.

a   b   c   d

17.

a   b   c   d

/ 17

Test 5

You have **10 minutes** to do this test. Circle the letter for each correct answer.

> Work out which 3D figure in the grey box has been rotated to make the new 3D figure.

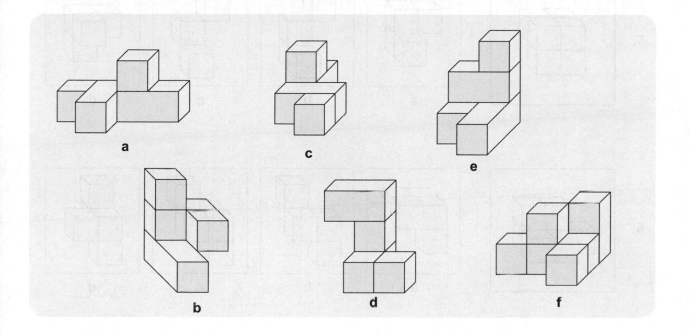

a

c

e

b

d

f

1.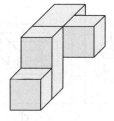

a   d

b   e

c   f

2.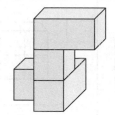

a   d

b   e

c   f

3.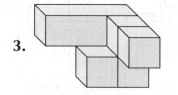

a   d

b   e

c   f

4.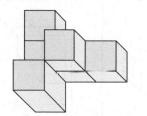

a   d

b   e

c   f

Without rotating the figure on the left, work out which option fits onto it to make the 3D shape in the grey box.

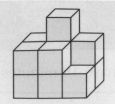

5.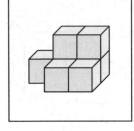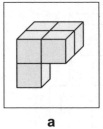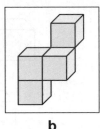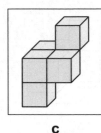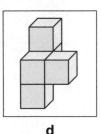

  a   b   c   d

6.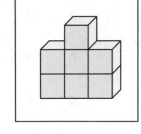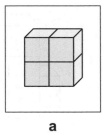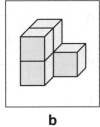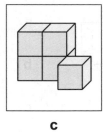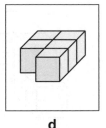

  a   b   c   d

7.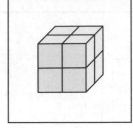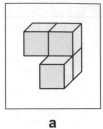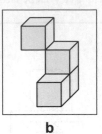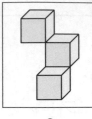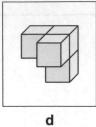

  a   b   c   d

8.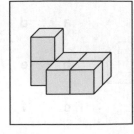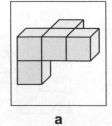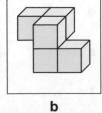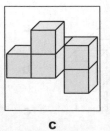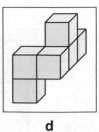

  a   b   c   d

The figures on the left show different views of the same cube. All the cube faces are different. Work out which of the options should replace the blue cube face.

9.

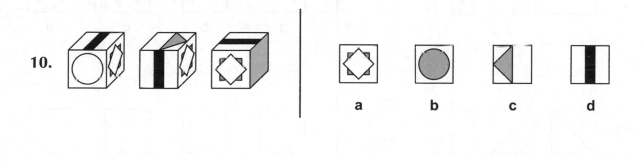

a   b   c   d

10.

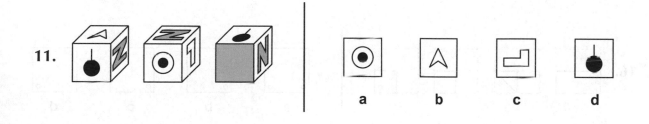

a   b   c   d

11.

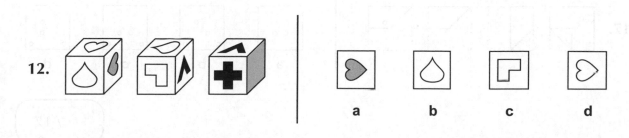

a   b   c   d

12.

a   b   c   d

Test 5

A square is folded and then a hole is punched, as shown on the left.
Work out which option shows the square when unfolded.

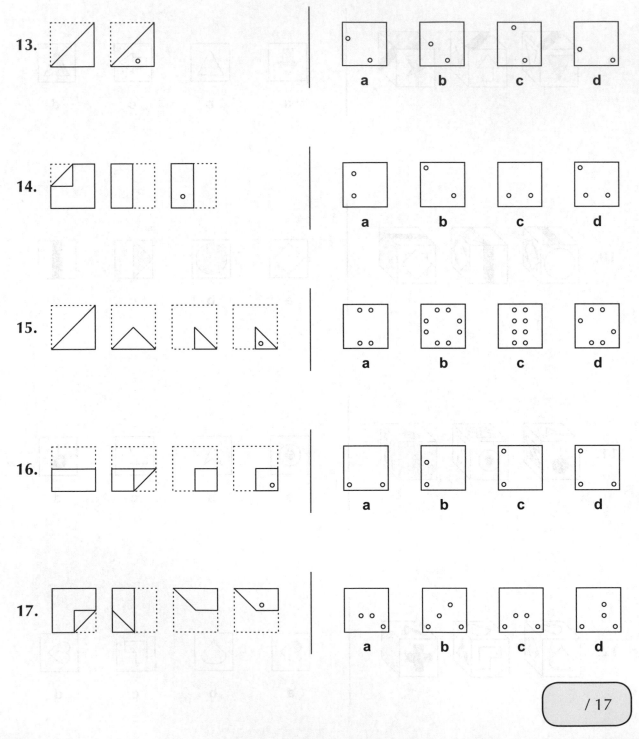

13.
    a   b   c   d

14.
    a   b   c   d

15.
    a   b   c   d

16.
    a   b   c   d

17.
    a   b   c   d

/ 17

You have **10 minutes** to do this test. Circle the letter for each correct answer.

Work out which option is a 2D view from **above** the 3D figure shown.

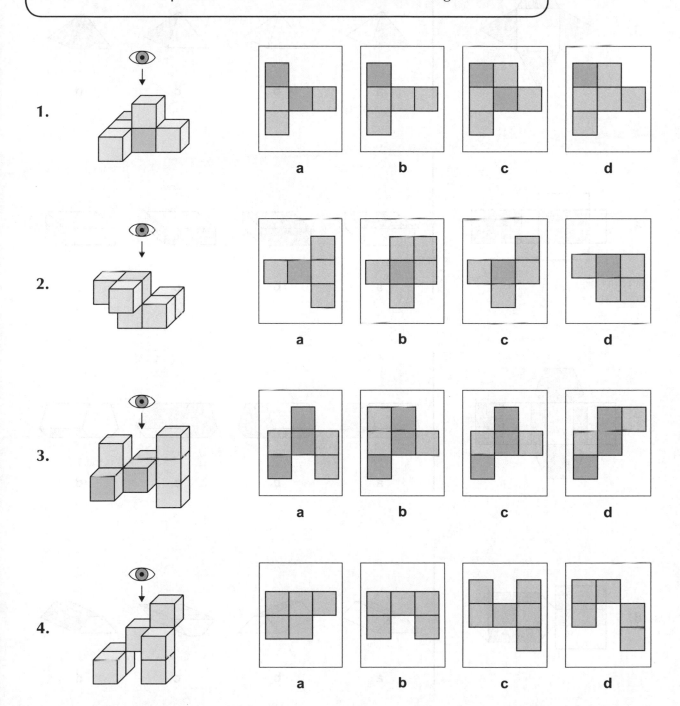

1.

a   b   c   d

2.

a   b   c   d

3.

a   b   c   d

4.

a   b   c   d

29

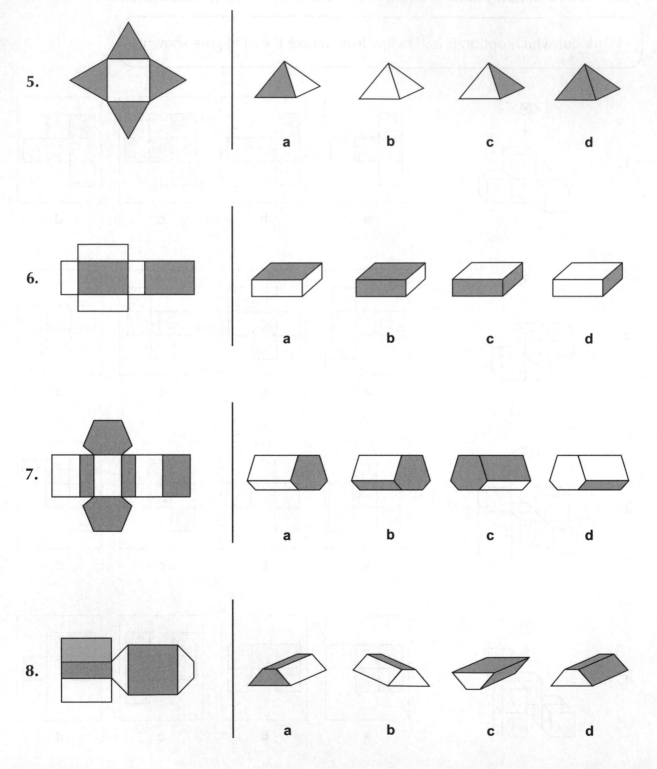

5.

a   b   c   d

6.

a   b   c   d

7.

a   b   c   d

8.

a   b   c   d

Work out which 3D figure in the grey box has been rotated to make the new 3D figure.

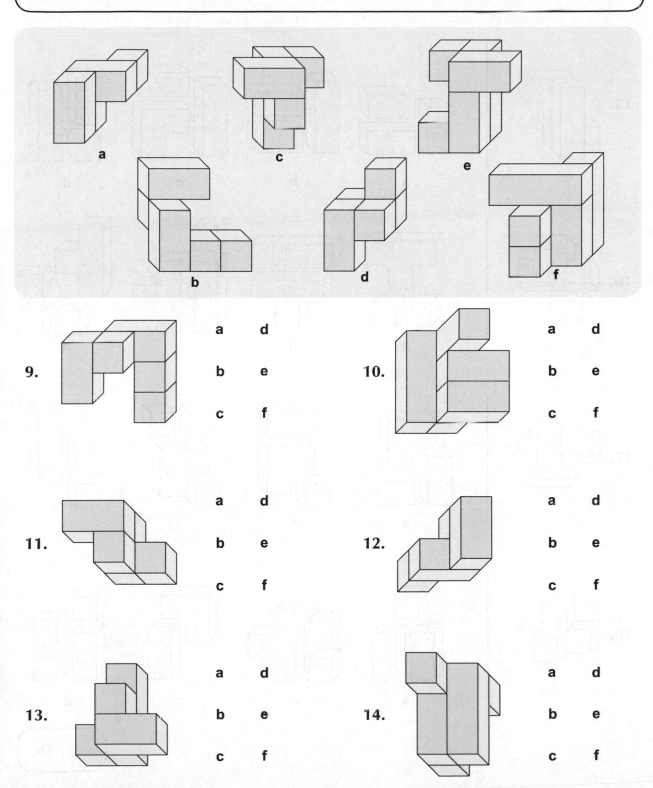

9.
    a   d
    b   e
    c   f

10.
    a   d
    b   e
    c   f

11.
    a   d
    b   e
    c   f

12.
    a   d
    b   e
    c   f

13.
    a   d
    b   e
    c   f

14.
    a   d
    b   e
    c   f

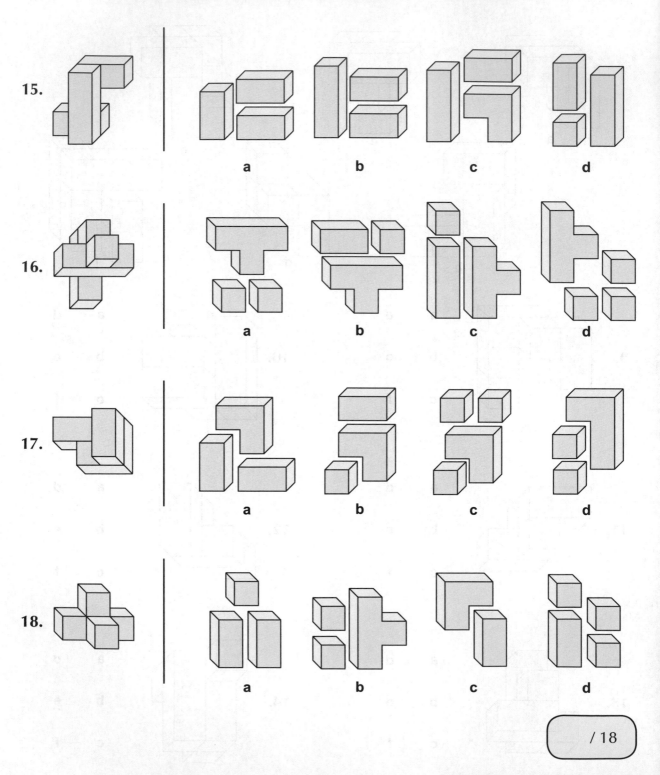

15.

a   b   c   d

16.

a   b   c   d

17.

a   b   c   d

18.

a   b   c   d

/ 18

32

These puzzles are an excellent way to practise **building blocks** and **nets**...

A Piece-a the Action

A wood-fired pizza oven
needs to be completed.

The pizza oven has to be four bricks tall
and must not have a roof.

There are three types of brick available.

How many of each type of brick
are needed to complete the oven,
using as few bricks as possible?

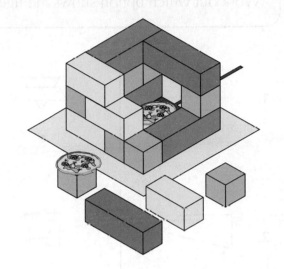

Like a Normal Dice, but More Pointy...

The net of an 8-sided dice is missing numbers from some faces.
Each side has a different number from 1 to 8.

Opposite faces on an 8-sided dice always add up to 9.

Can you complete the net for the 8-sided dice?

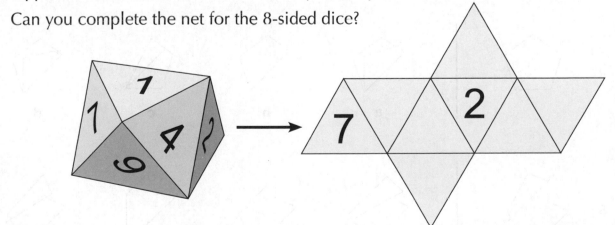

You have **10 minutes** to do this test. Circle the letter for each correct answer.

Work out which option shows the figure on the left when folded along the dotted line.

1.

                                                a   b   c   d

2.

                                                a   b   c   d

3.

                                                a   b   c   d

4.

                                                a   b   c   d

5.

                                                a   b   c   d

Without rotating the figure on the left, work out which option fits onto it to make the 3D shape in the grey box.

6.
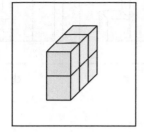 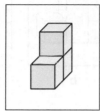 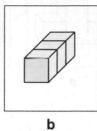 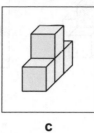 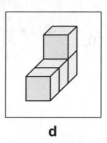

a   b   c   d

7.
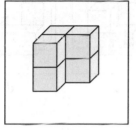 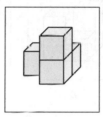 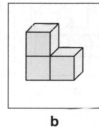 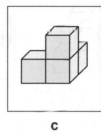 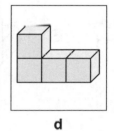

a   b   c   d

8.
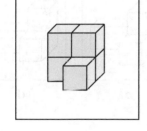 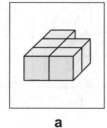 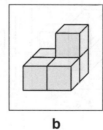 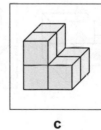 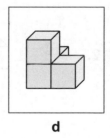

a   b   c   d

9.
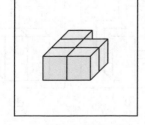 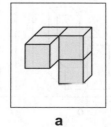 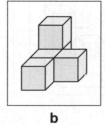 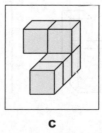 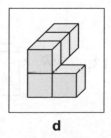

a   b   c   d

Test 7

Work out which option is the 3D figure viewed from the **left**.

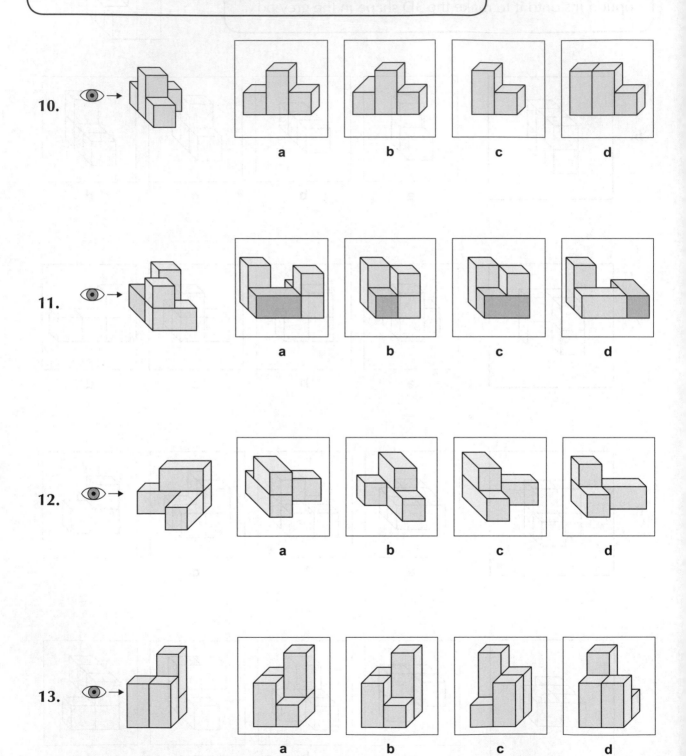

10.

a   b   c   d

11.

a   b   c   d

12.

a   b   c   d

13.

a   b   c   d

36

Work out which of the four cubes can be made from the net.

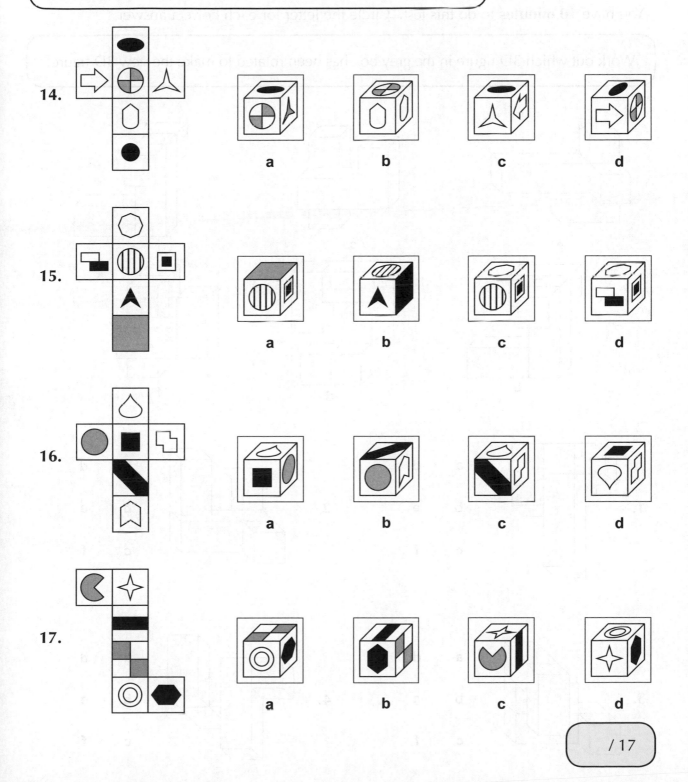

14.

a   b   c   d

15.

a   b   c   d

16.

a   b   c   d

17.

a   b   c   d

/ 17

37

Test 8

You have **10 minutes** to do this test. Circle the letter for each correct answer.

Work out which 3D figure in the grey box has been rotated to make the new 3D figure.

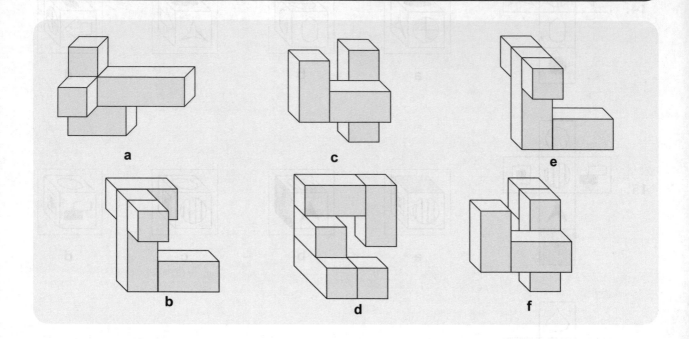

a

c

e

b

d

f

1.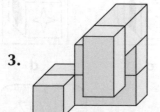

a	d
b	e
c	f

2.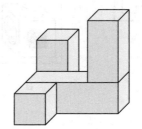

a	d
b	e
c	f

3.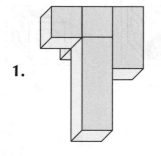

a	d
b	e
c	f

4.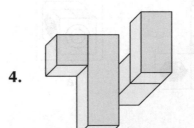

a	d
b	e
c	f

A square is folded and then a hole is punched, as shown on the left. Work out which option shows the square when unfolded.

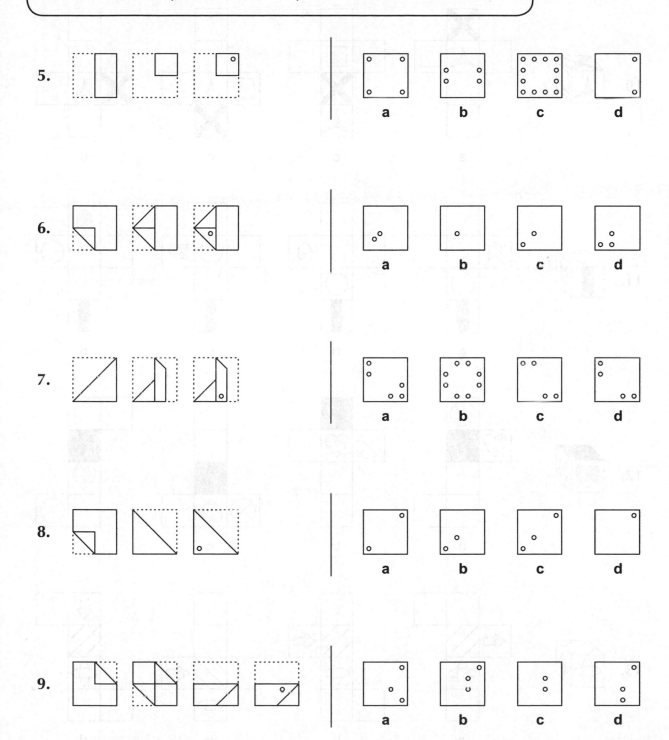

5.   a   b   c   d

6.   a   b   c   d

7.   a   b   c   d

8.   a   b   c   d

9.   a   b   c   d

39

Work out which of the four partial nets can be folded to make the cube on the left.

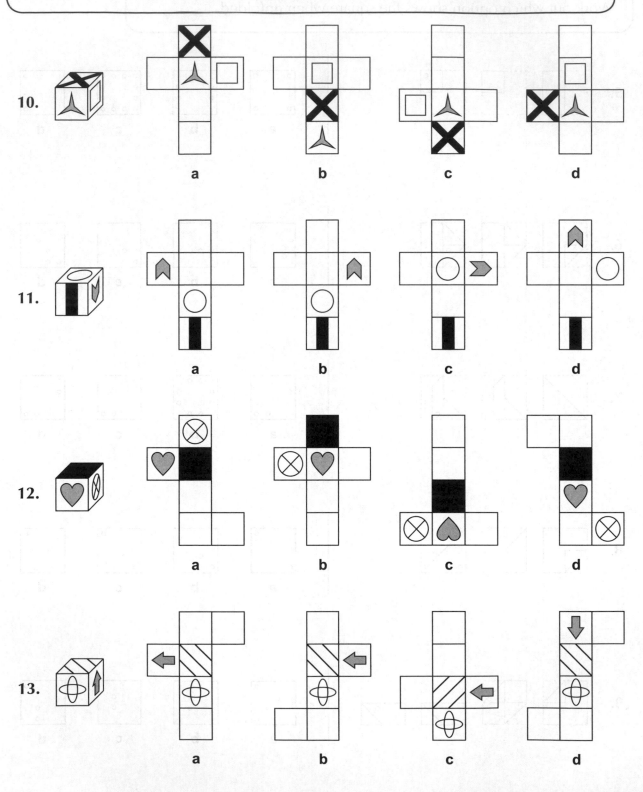

10.

a   b   c   d

11.

a   b   c   d

12.

a   b   c   d

13.

a   b   c   d

Work out which option is a 2D view from the **right** of the 3D figure shown.

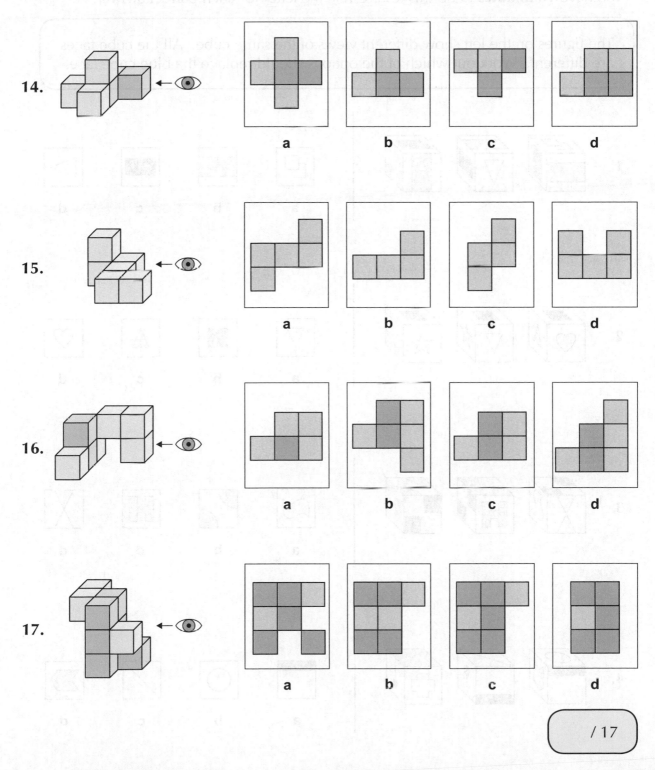

14.

a   b   c   d

15.

a   b   c   d

16.

a   b   c   d

17.

a   b   c   d

/ 17

41

You have **10 minutes** to do this test. Circle the letter for each correct answer.

The figures on the left show different views of the same cube. All the cube faces are different. Work out which of the options should replace the blue cube face.

1.

       a   b   c   d

2.

       a   b   c   d

3.

       a   b   c   d

4.

       a   b   c   d

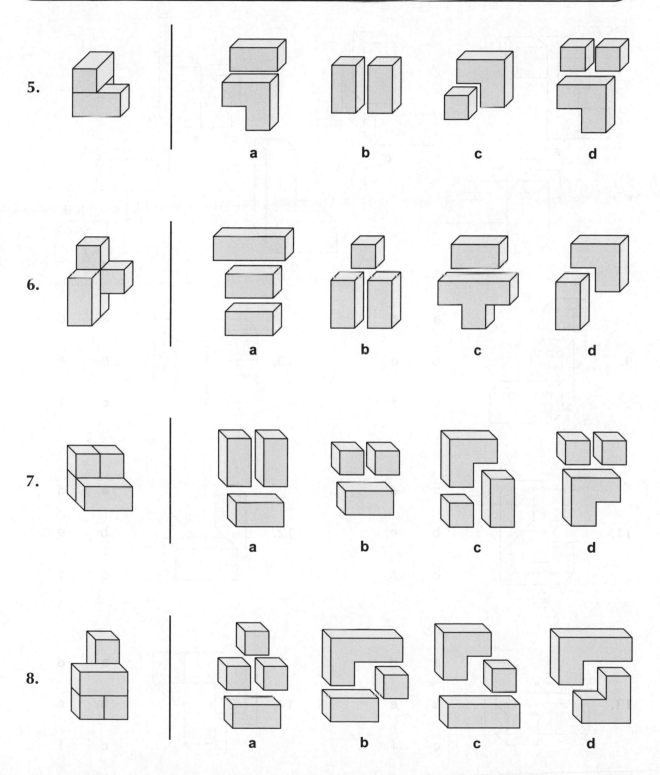

5.

a   b   c   d

6.

a   b   c   d

7.

a   b   c   d

8.

a   b   c   d

Test 9

Work out which 3D figure in the grey box has been rotated to make the new 3D figure.

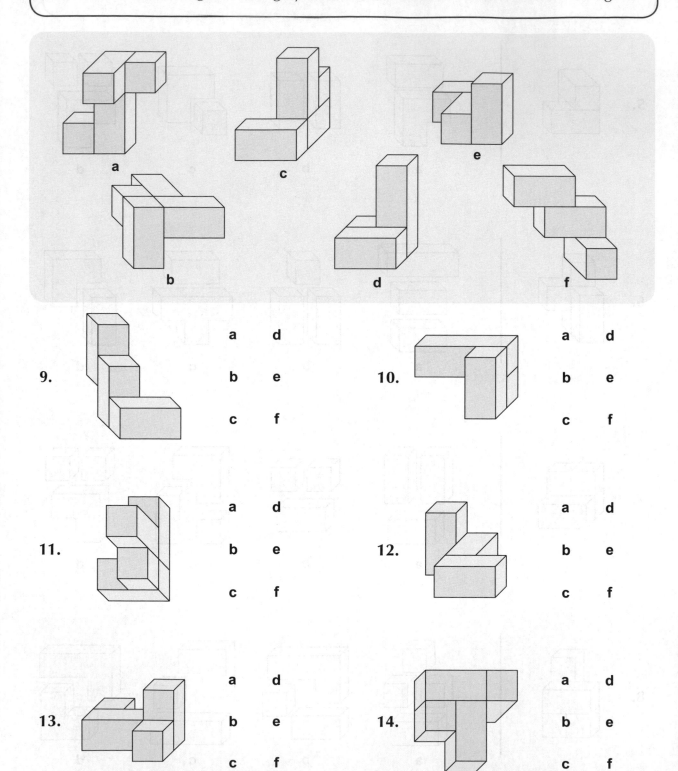

a

c

e

b

d

f

9.

a   d

b   e

c   f

10.

a   d

b   e

c   f

11.

a   d

b   e

c   f

12.

a   d

b   e

c   f

13.

a   d

b   e

c   f

14.

a   d

b   e

c   f

Work out which of the 3D shapes can be made from the net.

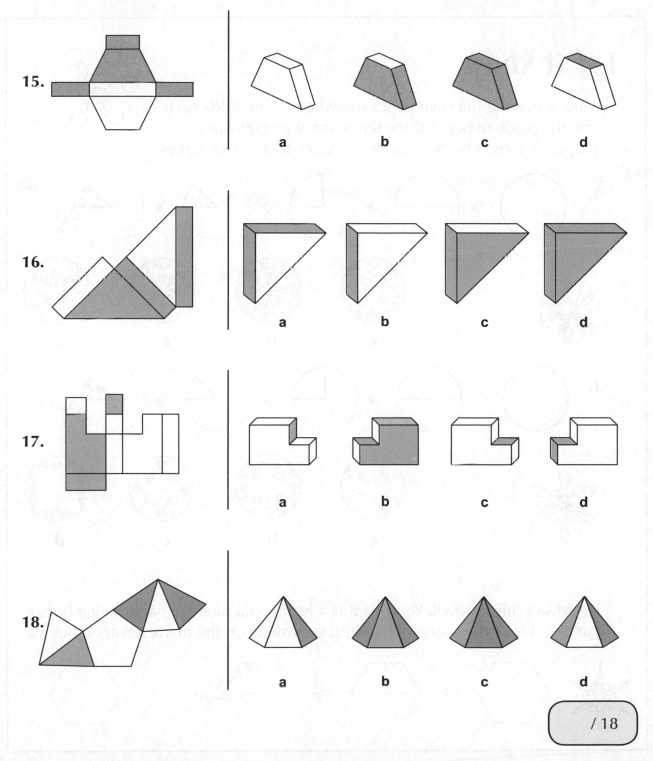

15.

a b c d

16.

a b c d

17.

a b c d

18.

a b c d

/ 18

45

Phew... break time! Have a go at these puzzles to practise your **fold and punch** skills.

Let it Snow

Misa is making her own paper snowflakes. She folds each circular piece of paper three times and then cuts out a shape, as shown below. Circle the snowflakes Misa makes.

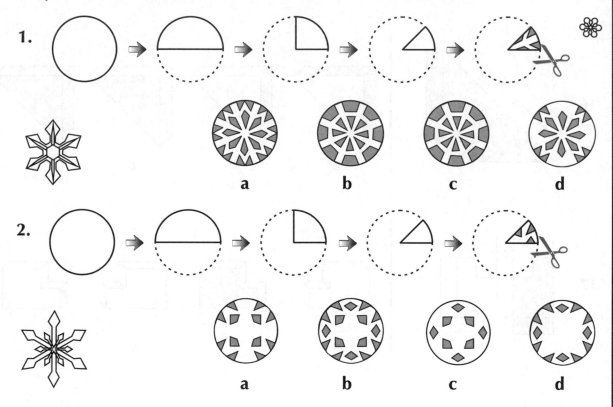

1.

a   **b**   **c**   **d**

2.

a   **b**   **c**   **d**

For Misa's third snowflake, she folds a hexagonal piece of paper twice before cutting. Draw the shape of her third snowflake on the blank hexagon below.

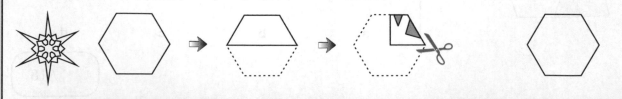

46

You have **10 minutes** to do this test. Circle the letter for each correct answer.

Work out which option is a 2D view from **above** the 3D figure shown.

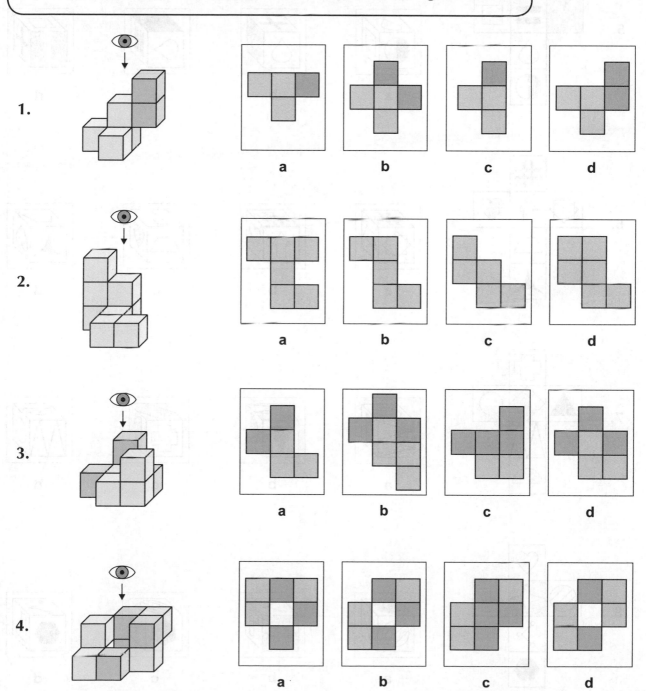

1.

    a   b   c   d

2.

    a   b   c   d

3.

    a   b   c   d

4.

    a   b   c   d

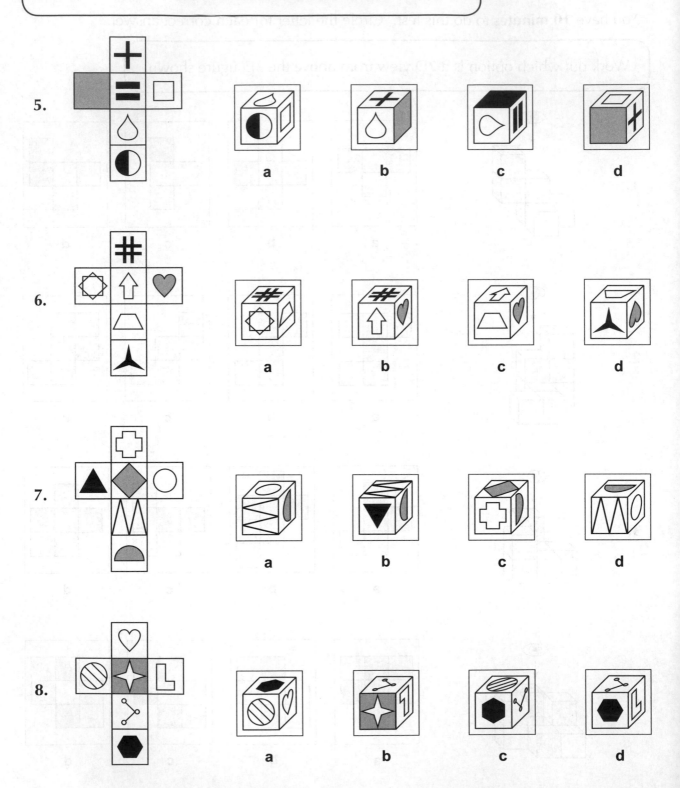

5.

a   b   c   d

6.

a   b   c   d

7.

a   b   c   d

8.

a   b   c   d

Work out which 3D figure in the grey box has been rotated to make the new 3D figure.

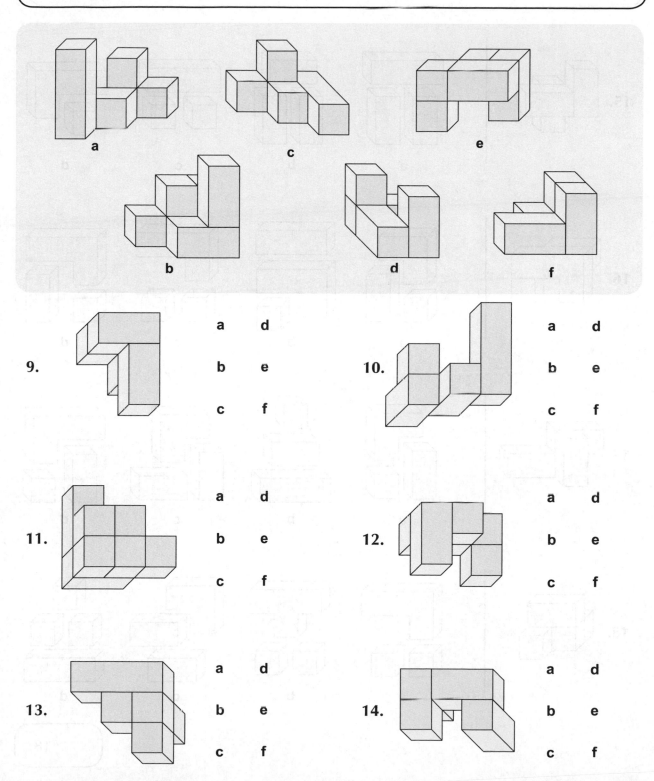

a

c

e

b

d

f

9.   a   d   b   e   c   f

10.   a   d   b   e   c   f

11.   a   d   b   e   c   f

12.   a   d   b   e   c   f

13.   a   d   b   e   c   f

14.   a   d   b   e   c   f

Work out which set of blocks can be put together to make the 3D figure on the left.

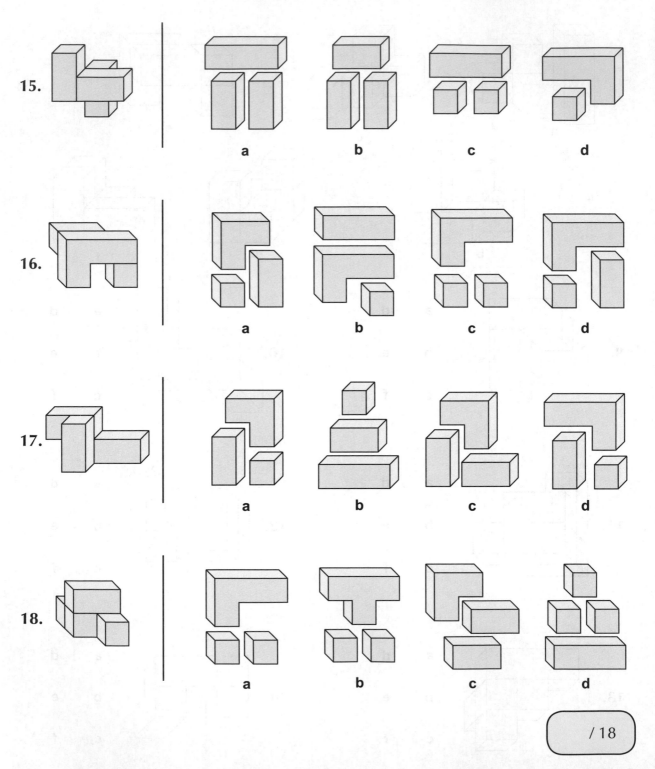

15.

a　　　b　　　c　　　d

16.

a　　　b　　　c　　　d

17.

a　　　b　　　c　　　d

18.

a　　　b　　　c　　　d

/ 18

50

You have **10 minutes** to do this test. Circle the letter for each correct answer.

Work out which option is the 3D figure viewed from the **left**.

1.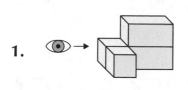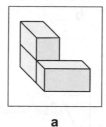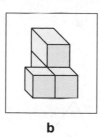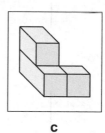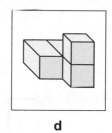

a   b   c   d

2.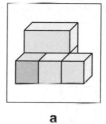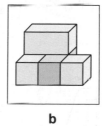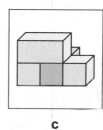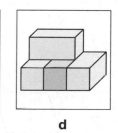

a   b   c   d

3.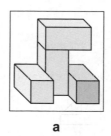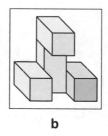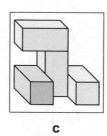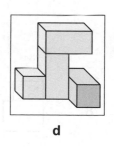

a   b   c   d

4.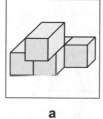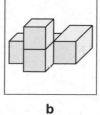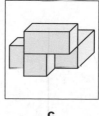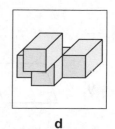

a   b   c   d

51

Work out which option shows the figure on the left when folded along the dotted line.

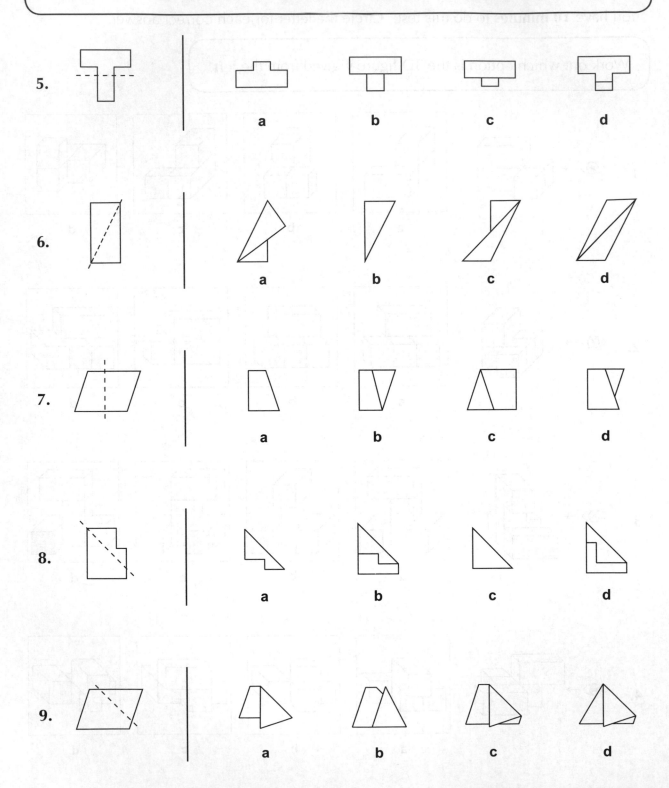

5.

a   b   c   d

6.

a   b   c   d

7.

a   b   c   d

8.

a   b   c   d

9.

a   b   c   d

The figures on the left show different views of the same cube. All the cube faces are different. Work out which of the options should replace the blue cube face.

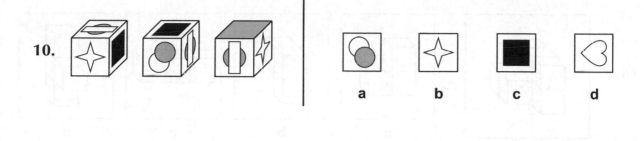

10.

    a   b   c   d

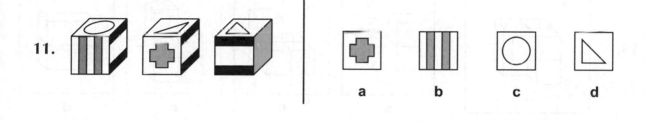

11.

    a   b   c   d

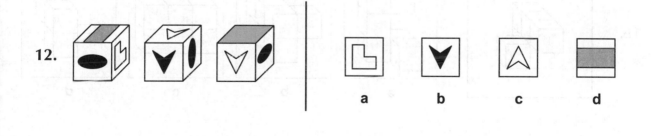

12.

    a   b   c   d

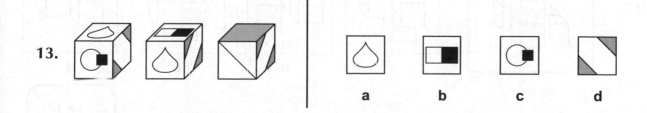

13.

    a   b   c   d

53

Without rotating the figure on the left, work out which option fits onto it to make the 3D shape in the grey box.

14.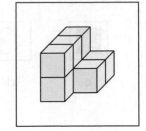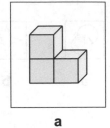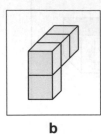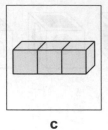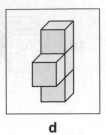

  a   b   c   d

15.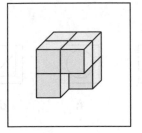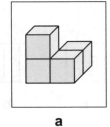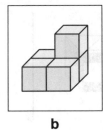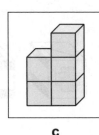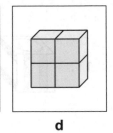

  a   b   c   d

16.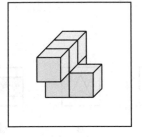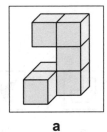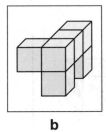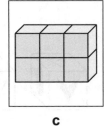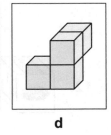

  a   b   c   d

17.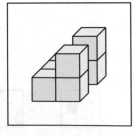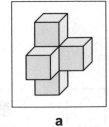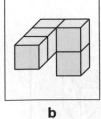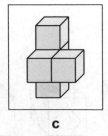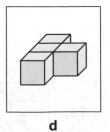

  a   b   c   d

54

You have **10 minutes** to do this test. Circle the letter for each correct answer.

Work out which option is the 3D figure viewed from the **right**.

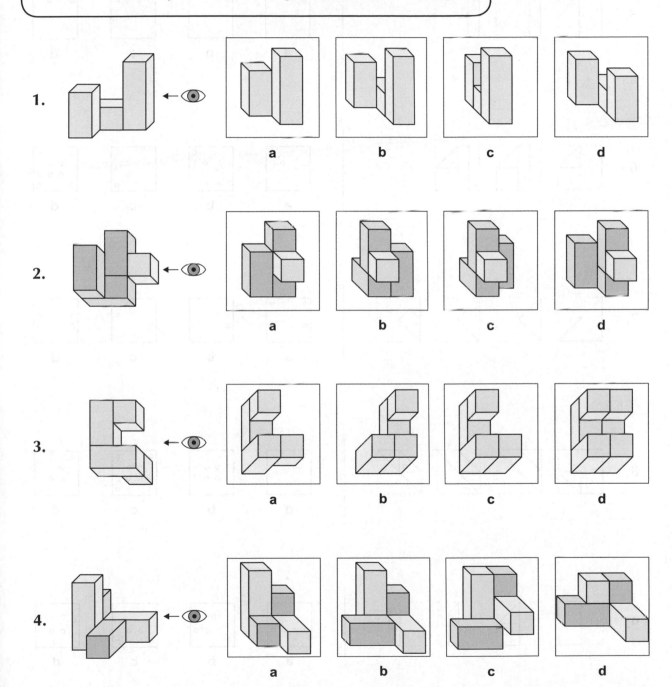

1.
    a   b   c   d

2.
    a   b   c   d

3.
    a   b   c   d

4.
    a   b   c   d

A square is folded and then a hole is punched, as shown on the left.
Work out which option shows the square when unfolded.

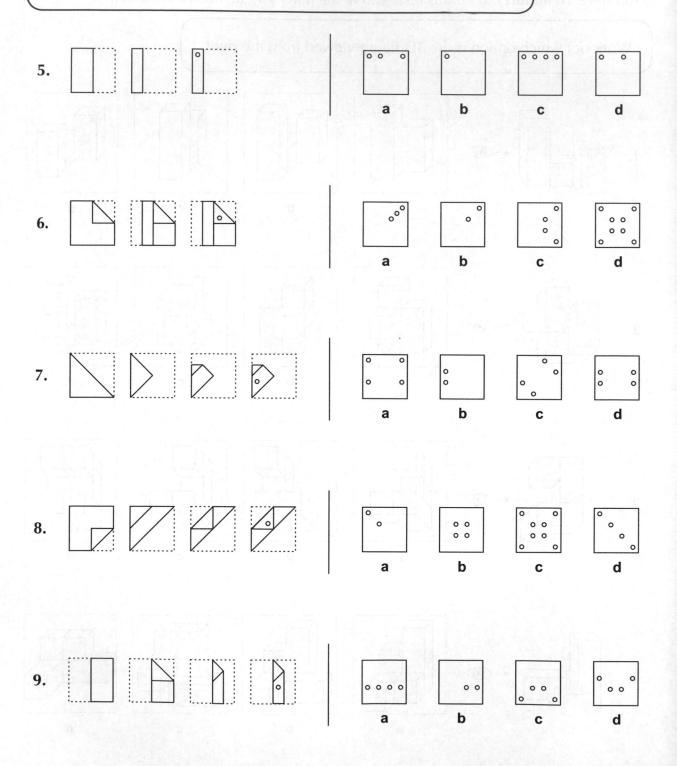

5.   a   b   c   d

6.   a   b   c   d

7.   a   b   c   d

8.   a   b   c   d

9.   a   b   c   d

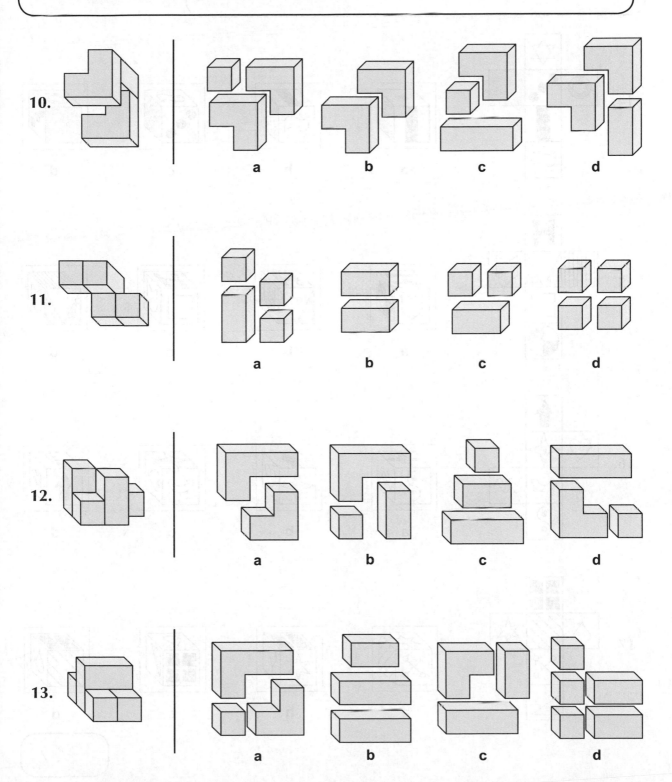

10.

a   b   c   d

11.

a   b   c   d

12.

a   b   c   d

13.

a   b   c   d

Work out which of the four cubes can be made from the net.

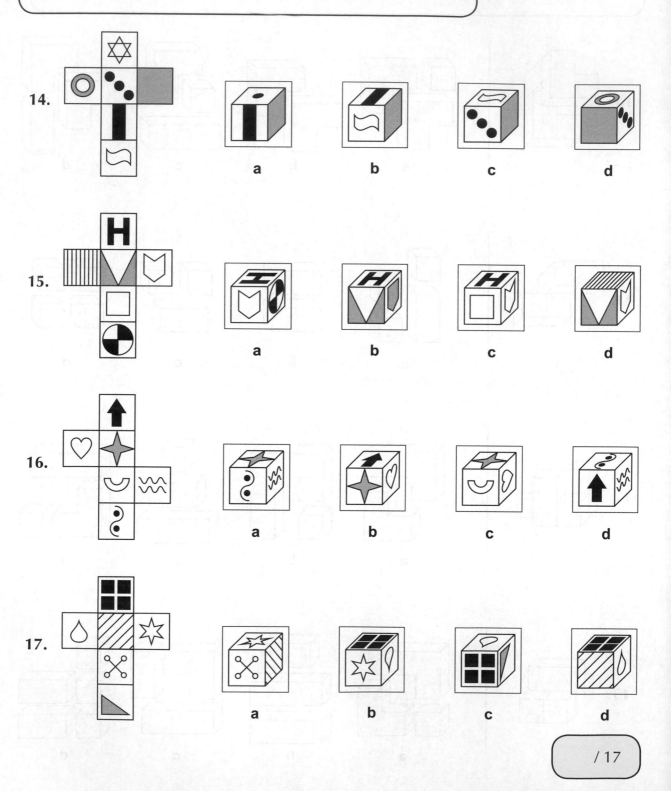

14.

a   b   c   d

15.

a   b   c   d

16.

a   b   c   d

17.

a   b   c   d

/ 17

Here's a page of puzzles to help you practise **3D views** and **2D views**. Hoorah!

The Rear End of an Elephant

Micaela has built an elephant out of building blocks, as shown to the right. She turns it 90 degrees from right-to-left. What does the elephant look like now?

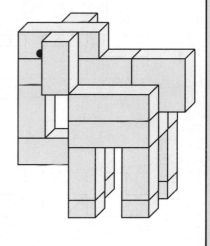

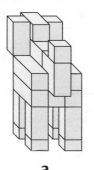
a

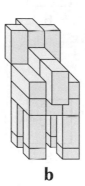
b

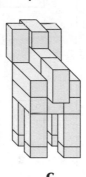
c

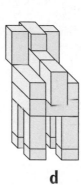
d

That's A-maze-ing...

Albert has created a 3D maze. He draws a 2D map of his maze on a grid. Finish his 2D map by shading in the right squares to match his maze.

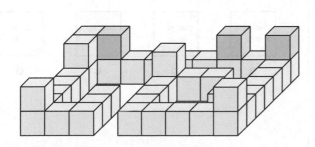

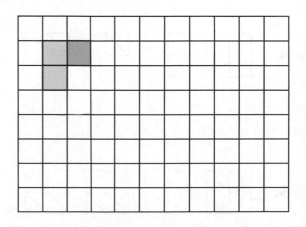

You have **10 minutes** to do this test. Circle the letter for each correct answer.

> A square is folded and then a hole is punched, as shown on the left.
> Work out which option shows the square when unfolded.

1.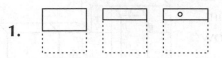

                                  a   **b**   **c**   **d**

2.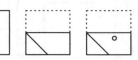

                                  a   **b**   **c**   **d**

3.

                                  a   **b**   **c**   **d**

4.

                                  a   **b**   **c**   **d**

5.

                                  a   **b**   **c**   **d**

Work out which of the 3D shapes can be made from the net.

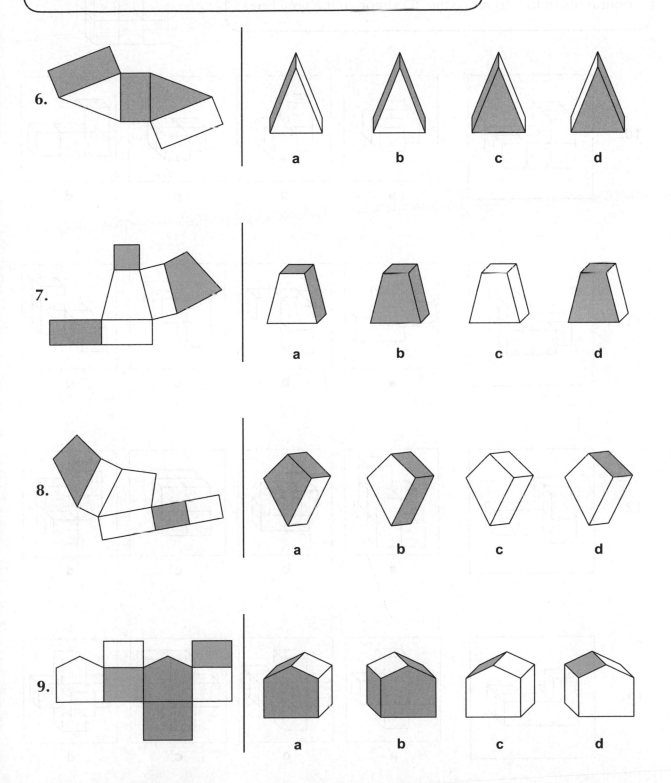

6.

a   b   c   d

7.

a   b   c   d

8.

a   b   c   d

9.

a   b   c   d

Without rotating the figure on the left, work out which option fits onto it to make the 3D shape in the grey box.

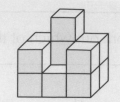

10.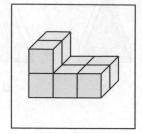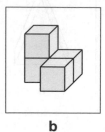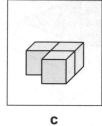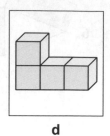

          a   b   c   d

11.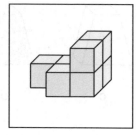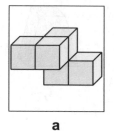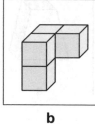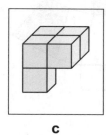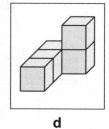

          a   b   c   d

12.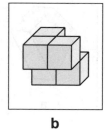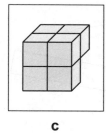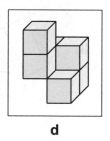

          a   b   c   d

13.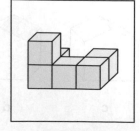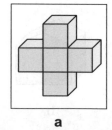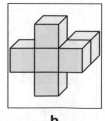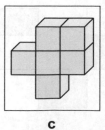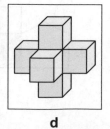

          a   b   c   d

Work out which 3D figure in the grey box has been rotated to make the new 3D figure.

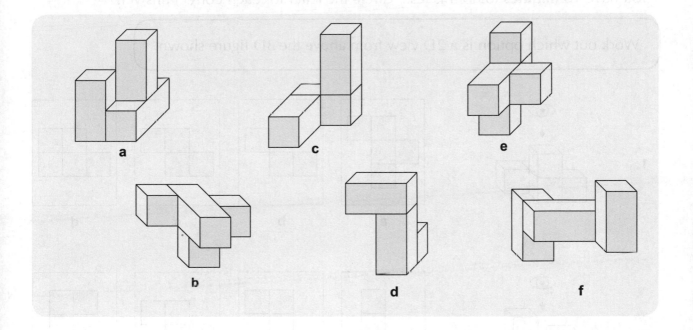

a

c

e

b

d

f

14.
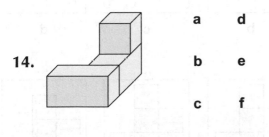

a   d

b   e

c   f

15.
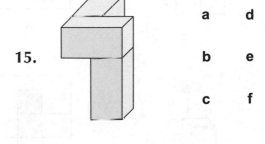

a   d

b   e

c   f

16.
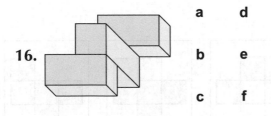

a   d

b   e

c   f

17.
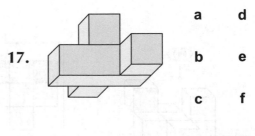

a   d

b   e

c   f

/ 17

Test 13

You have **10 minutes** to do this test. Circle the letter for each correct answer.

Work out which option is a 2D view from **above** the 3D figure shown.

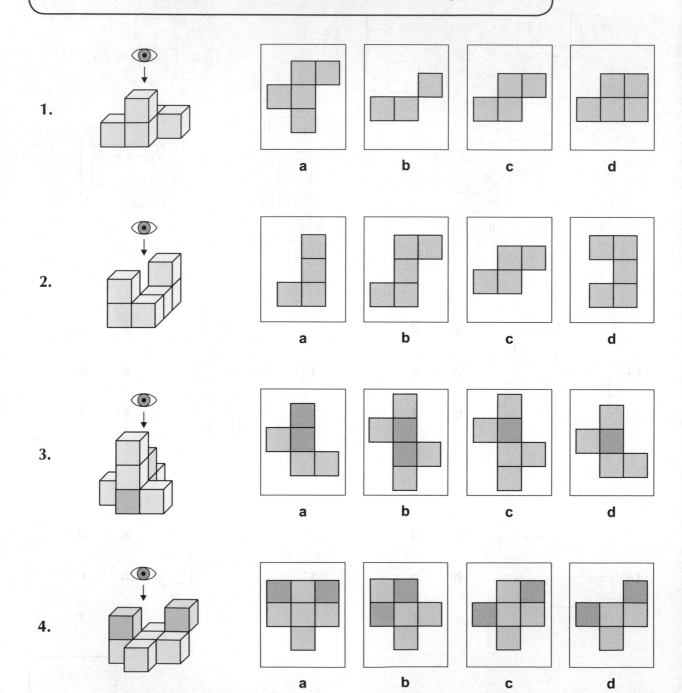

1. a b c d

2. a b c d

3. a b c d

4. a b c d

64

Work out which of the four partial nets can be folded to make the cube on the left.

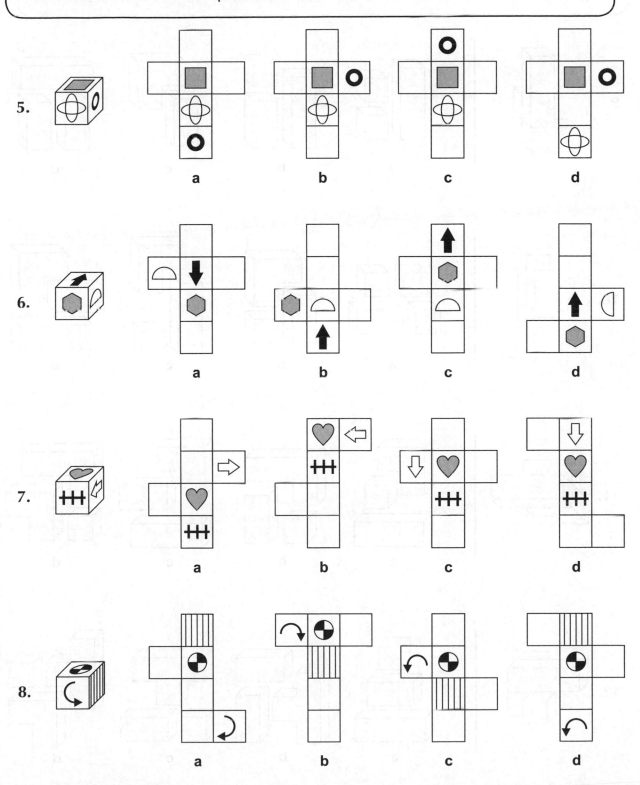

5.

a b c d

6.

a b c d

7.

a b c d

8.

a b c d

Test 14

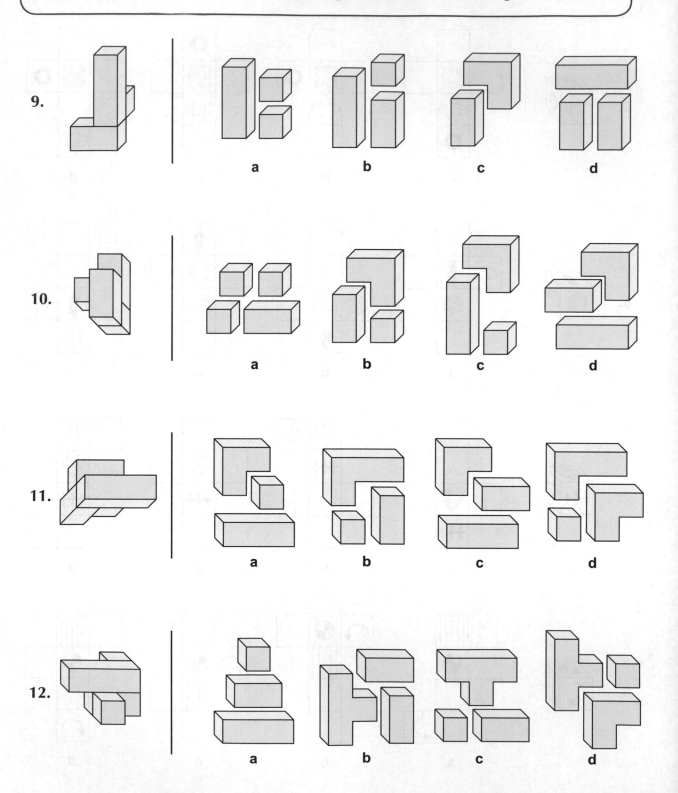

9.

a

b

c

d

10.

a

b

c

d

11.

a

b

c

d

12.

a

b

c

d

66

Work out which option shows the figure on the left when folded along the dotted line.

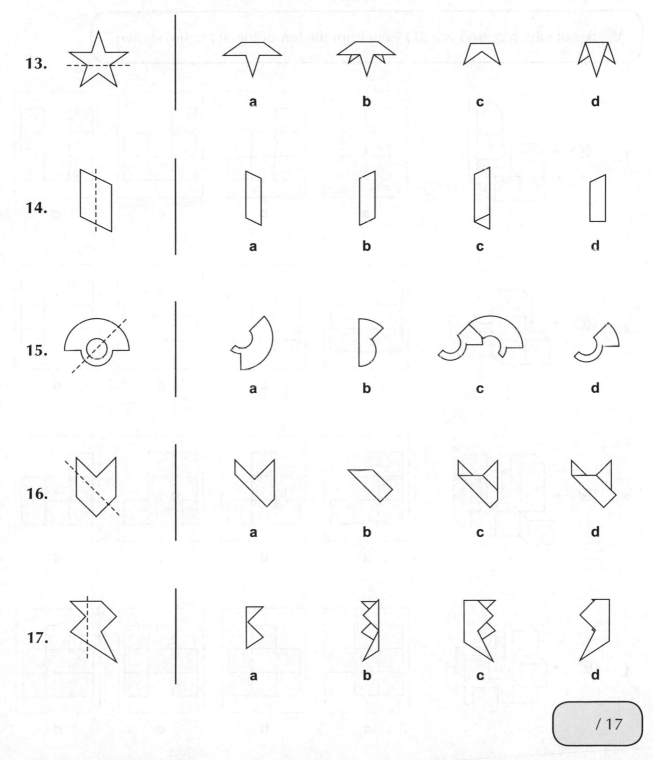

13.

   a   b   c   d

14.

   a   b   c   d

15.

   a   b   c   d

16.

   a   b   c   d

17.

   a   b   c   d

/ 17

Test 14

Test 15

You have **10 minutes** to do this test. Circle the letter for each correct answer.

Work out which option is a 2D view from the **left** of the 3D figure shown.

1.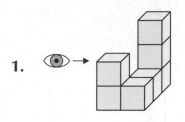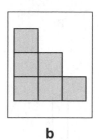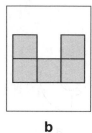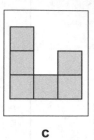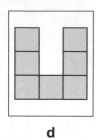

              a   b   c   d

2.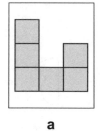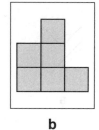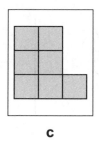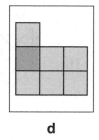

              a   b   c   d

3.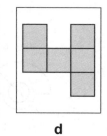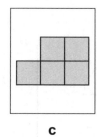

              a   b   c   d

4.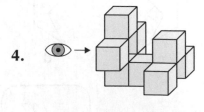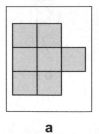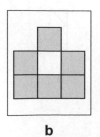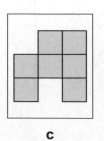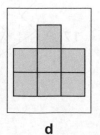

              a   b   c   d

68

Without rotating the figure on the left, work out which option fits onto it to make the 3D shape in the grey box.

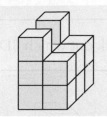

5.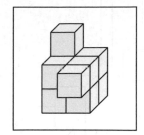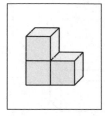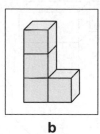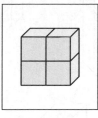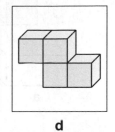

     a   b   c   d

6.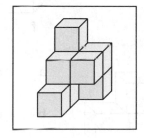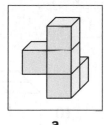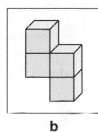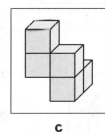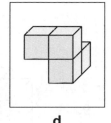

     a   b   c   d

7.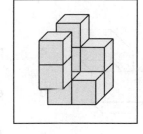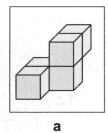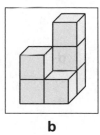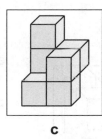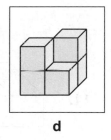

     a   b   c   d

8.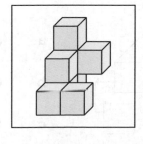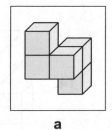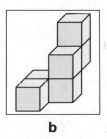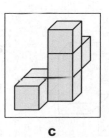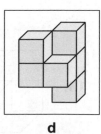

     a   b   c   d

69

Work out which 3D figure in the grey box has been rotated to make the new 3D figure.

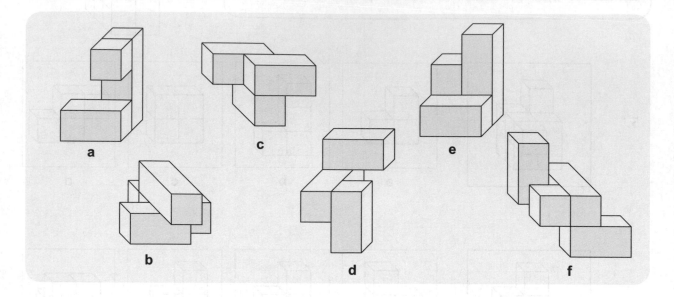

a

c

e

b

d

f

9.

a   d

b   e

c   f

10.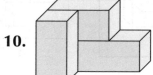

a   d

b   e

c   f

11.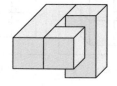

a   d

b   e

c   f

12.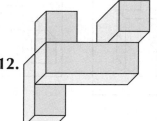

a   d

b   e

c   f

13.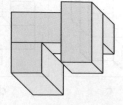

a   d

b   e

c   f

14.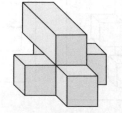

a   d

b   e

c   f

Work out which of the four cubes can be made from the net.

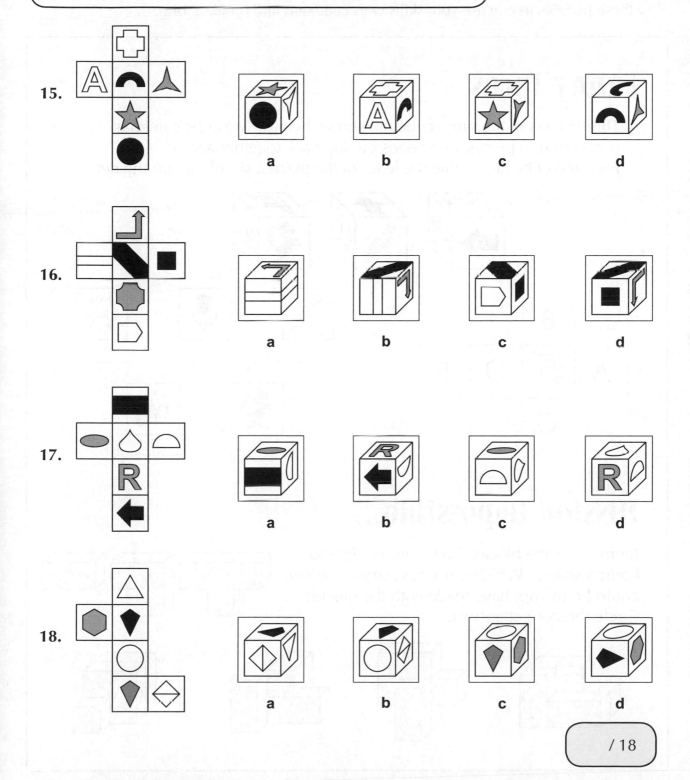

15.

a   b   c   d

16.

a   b   c   d

17.

a   b   c   d

18.

a   b   c   d

/ 18

Test 15

Try these puzzles to practise your skills with **cube nets** and **building blocks**.

Funny Faces

Three views of the same cube are shown below. The cube's net has been cut into pieces, and needs putting back together again.
For each cube face, write the letter of the place it should go on the net.

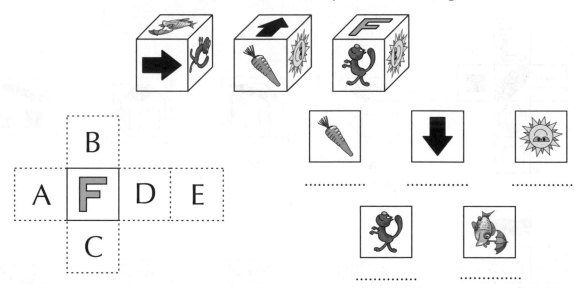

Mission Impossible...

Jimmy uses the blocks shown on the right to build a shape. Which one of the shapes below could Jimmy <u>not</u> have made with the blocks? Circle the correct answer.

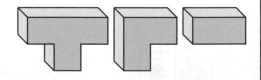

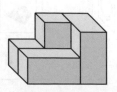
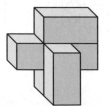
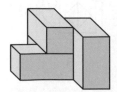
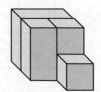

72

Test 16

You have **10 minutes** to do this test. Circle the letter for each correct answer.

Work out which option is a 2D view from the **right** of the 3D figure shown.

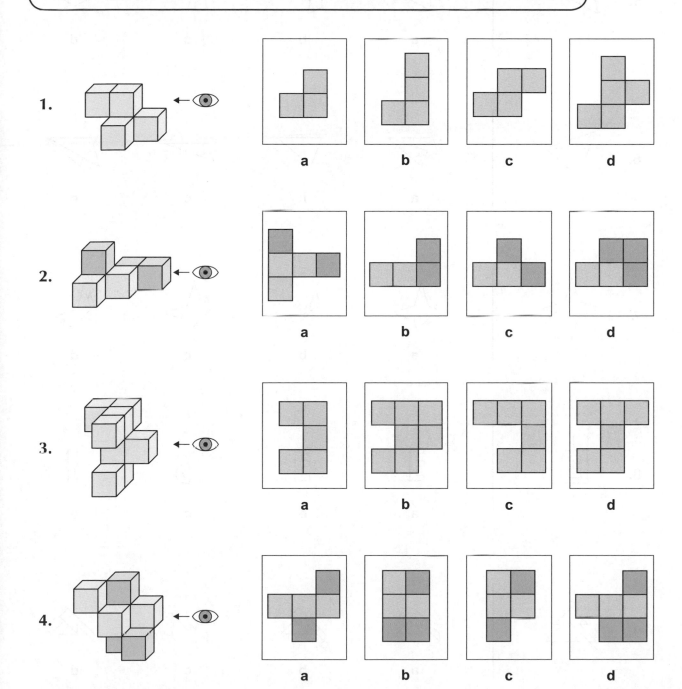

1.

2.

3.

4.

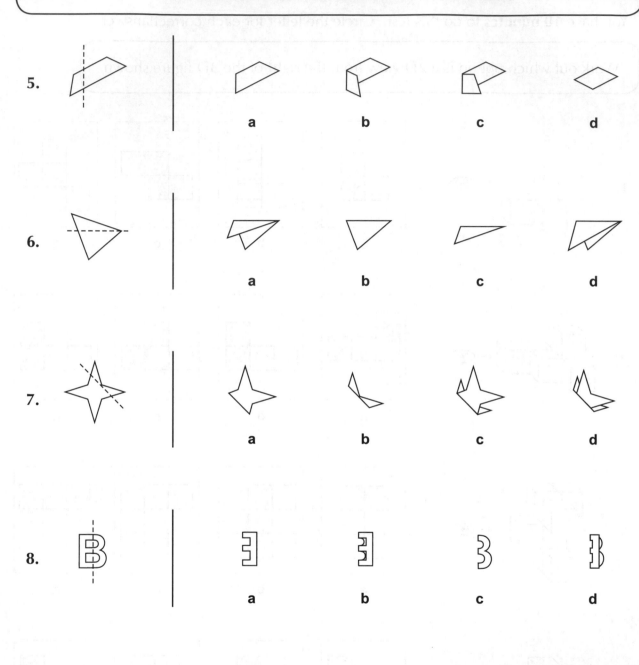

5.

a   b   c   d

6.

a   b   c   d

7.

a   b   c   d

8.

a   b   c   d

9.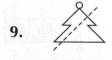

a   b   c   d

Without rotating the figure on the left, work out which option fits onto it to make the 3D shape in the grey box.

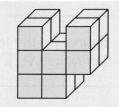

10.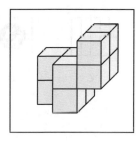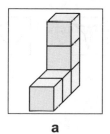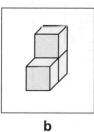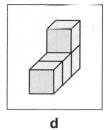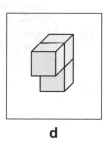

a   b   c   d

11.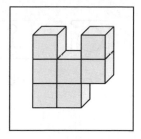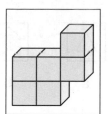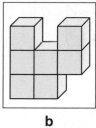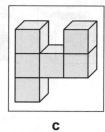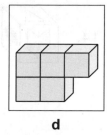

a   b   c   d

12.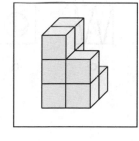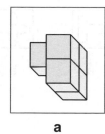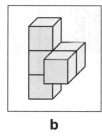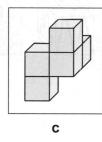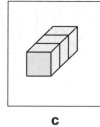

a   b   c   d

13.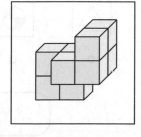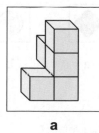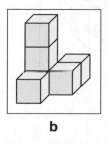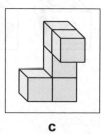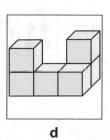

a   b   c   d

75

The figures on the left show different views of the same cube. All the cube faces are different. Work out which of the options should replace the blue cube face.

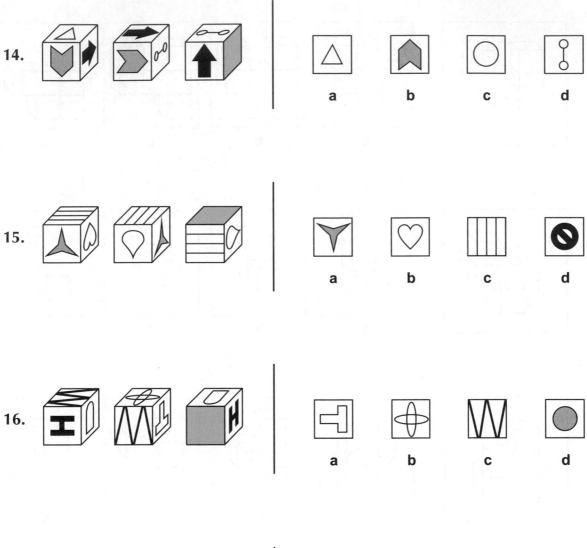

14.

    a   b   c   d

15.

    a   b   c   d

16.

    a   b   c   d

17.

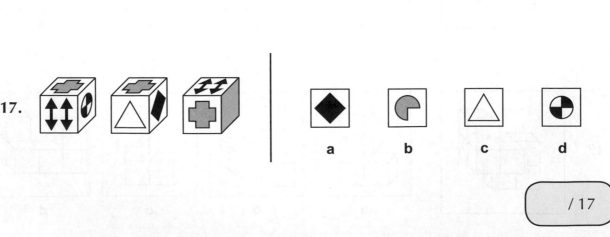

    a   b   c   d

/ 17

You have **10 minutes** to do this test. Circle the letter for each correct answer.

Work out which option is a 2D view from the **left** of the 3D figure shown.

1.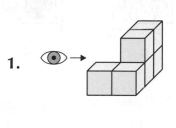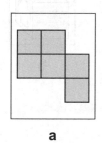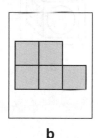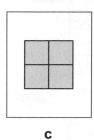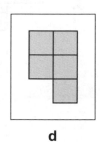

               a   b   c   d

2.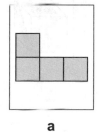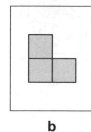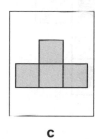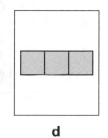

               a   b   c   d

3.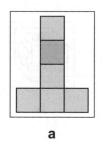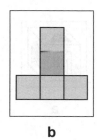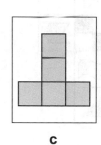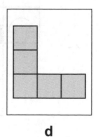

               a   b   c   d

4.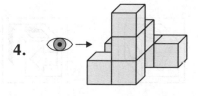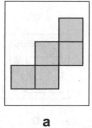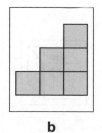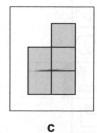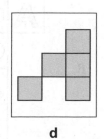

               a   b   c   d

Work out which of the four cubes can be made from the net.

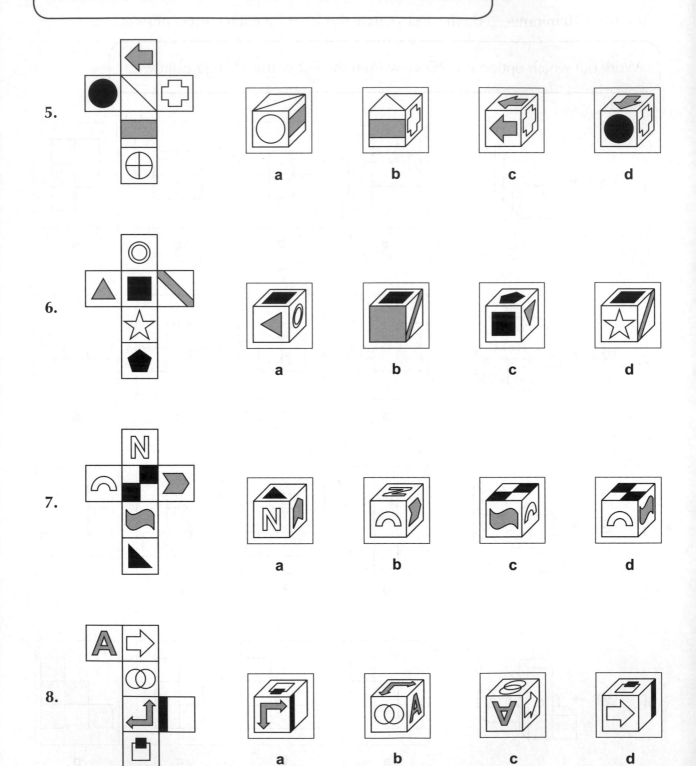

5.

a   b   c   d

6.

a   b   c   d

7.

a   b   c   d

8.

a   b   c   d

A square is folded and then a hole is punched, as shown on the left.
Work out which option shows the square when unfolded.

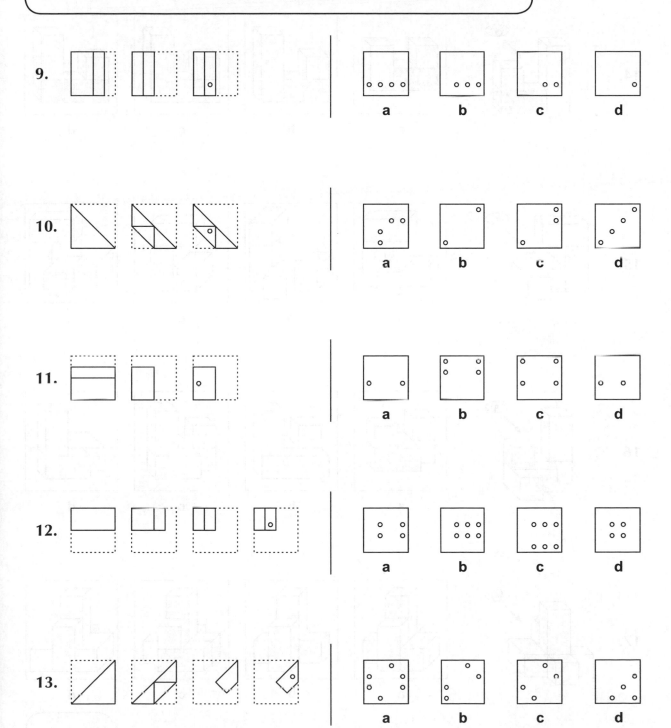

9.

a   b   c   d

10.

a   b   c   d

11.

a   b   c   d

12.

a   b   c   d

13.

a   b   c   d

79

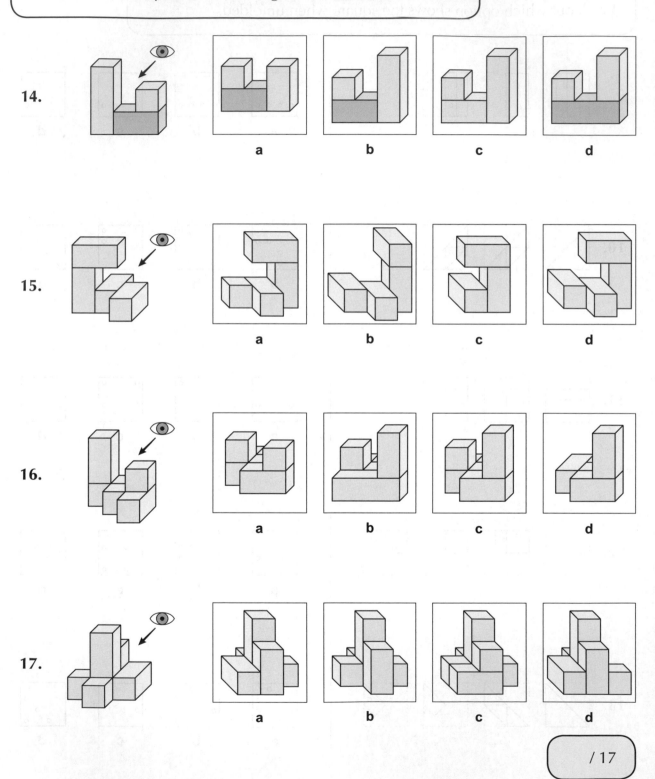

14.

a b c d

15.

a b c d

16.

a b c d

17.

a b c d

/ 17

80

You have **10 minutes** to do this test. Circle the letter for each correct answer.

Work out which set of blocks can be put together to make the 3D figure on the left.

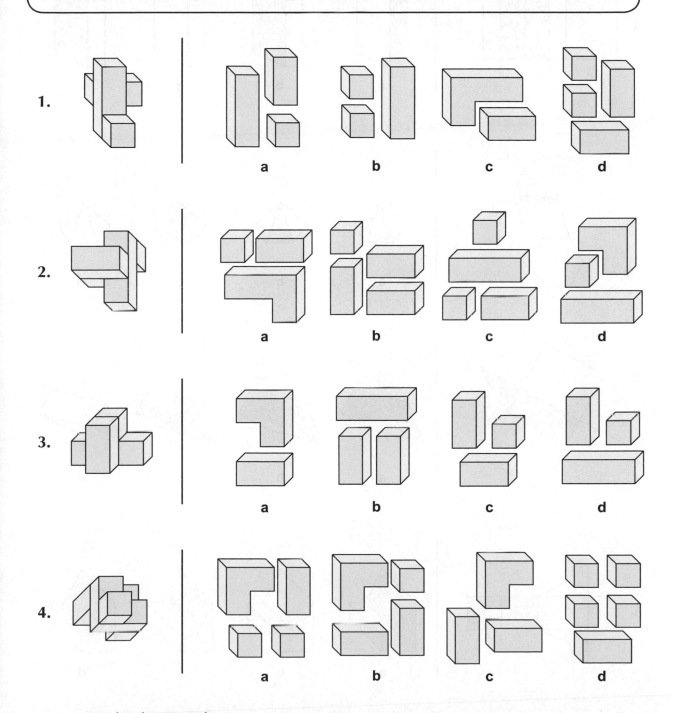

1.   a   b   c   d

2.   a   b   c   d

3.   a   b   c   d

4.   a   b   c   d

Work out which of the 3D shapes can be made from the net.

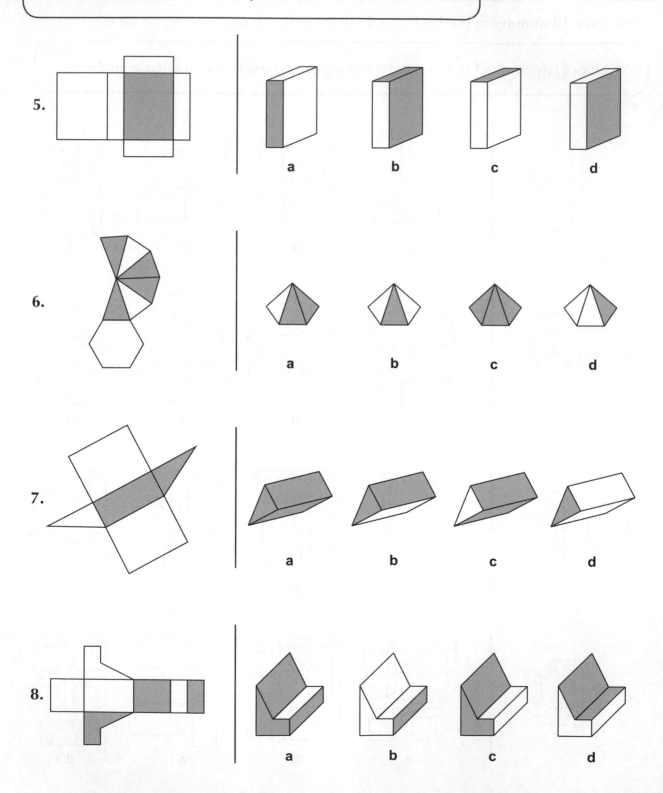

5.

a   b   c   d

6.

a   b   c   d

7.

a   b   c   d

8.

a   b   c   d

Work out which 3D figure in the grey box has been rotated to make the new 3D figure.

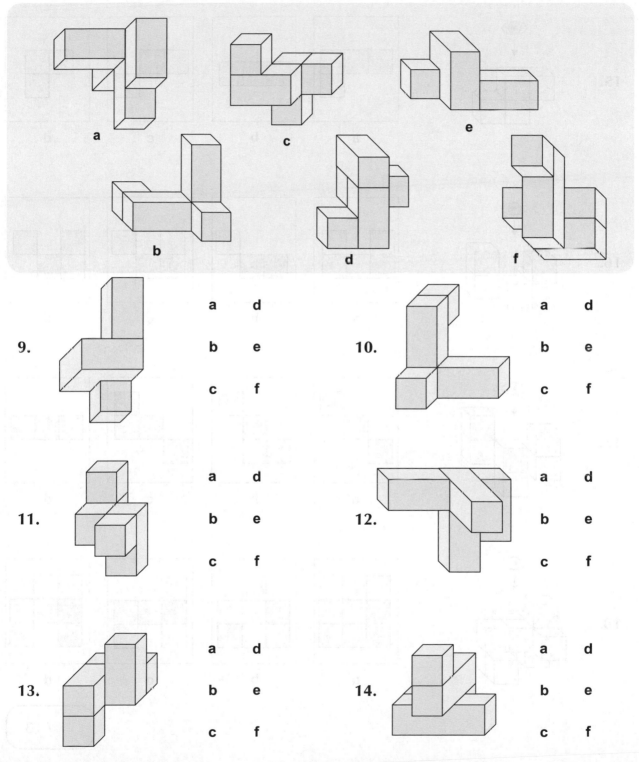

9.

a	d
b	e
c	f

10.

a	d
b	e
c	f

11.

a	d
b	e
c	f

12.

a	d
b	e
c	f

13.

a	d
b	e
c	f

14.

a	d
b	e
c	f

Test 18

Work out which option is a 2D view from **above** the 3D figure shown.

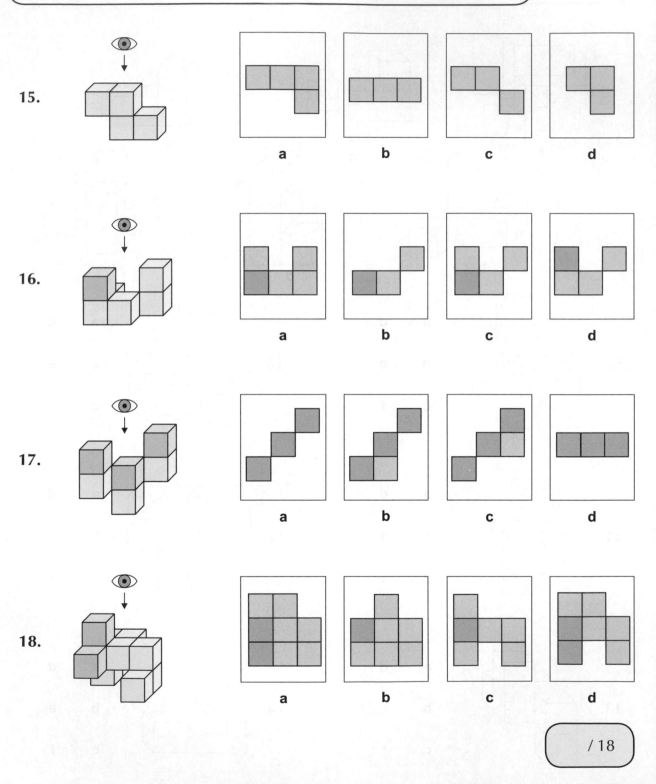

15.

a   b   c   d

16.

a   b   c   d

17.

a   b   c   d

18.

a   b   c   d

/ 18

It's your lucky day — this page is full of puzzles to help you practise **shaded nets**.

That's a Wrap

Kate wants each face of a birthday present to be covered in a different style of wrapping paper. She makes a net to fold around the present.

Finish the net to show the wrapping paper she uses for each face.

Front view   **Back view**

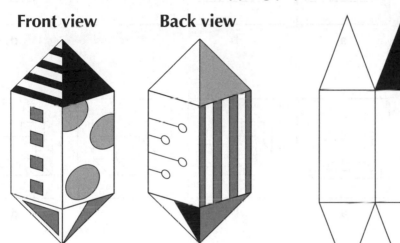

Let the Good Times Roll...

Matthew's ten-sided ornament is shown below from two different directions. It has 2 grey faces, 4 black faces, 2 blue faces and 2 spotted faces. Finish the net of his ornament below.

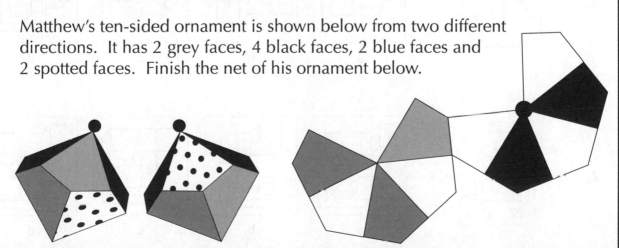

You have **10 minutes** to do this test. Circle the letter for each correct answer.

Work out which option is the 3D figure viewed from **above**.

1.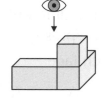

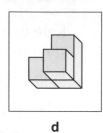

a   b   c   d

2.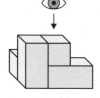

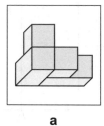 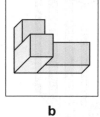 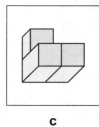 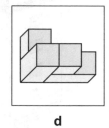

a   b   c   d

3.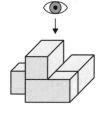

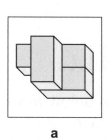 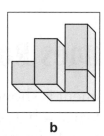 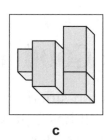 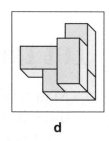

a   b   c   d

4.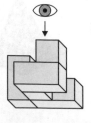

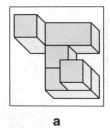 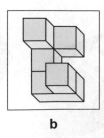 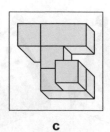 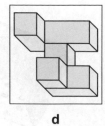

a   b   c   d

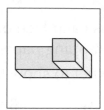

A square is folded and then a hole is punched, as shown on the left.
Work out which option shows the square when unfolded.

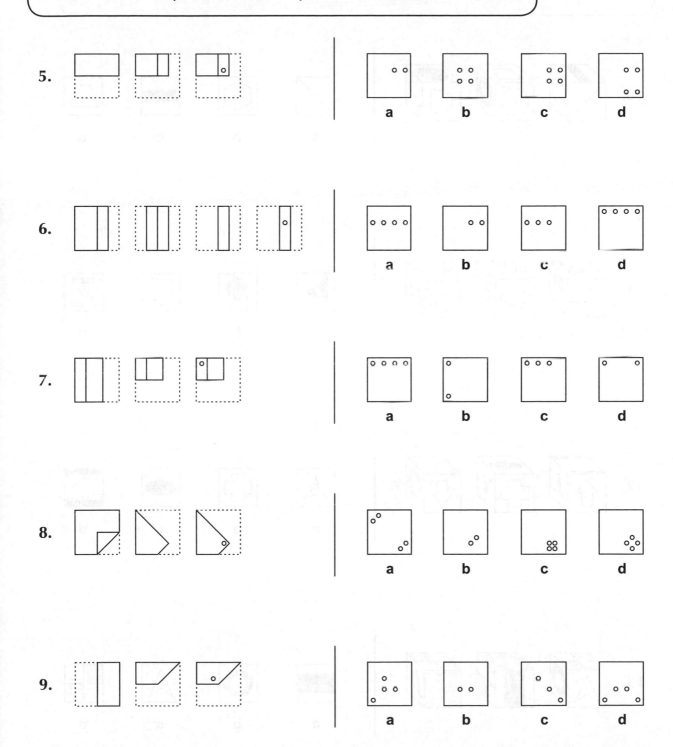

5.

      a   **b**   **c**   **d**

6.

      a   **b**   **c**   **d**

7.

      a   **b**   **c**   **d**

8.

      a   **b**   **c**   **d**

9.

      a   **b**   **c**   **d**

Test 19

The figures on the left show different views of the same cube. All the cube faces are different. Work out which of the options should replace the blue cube face.

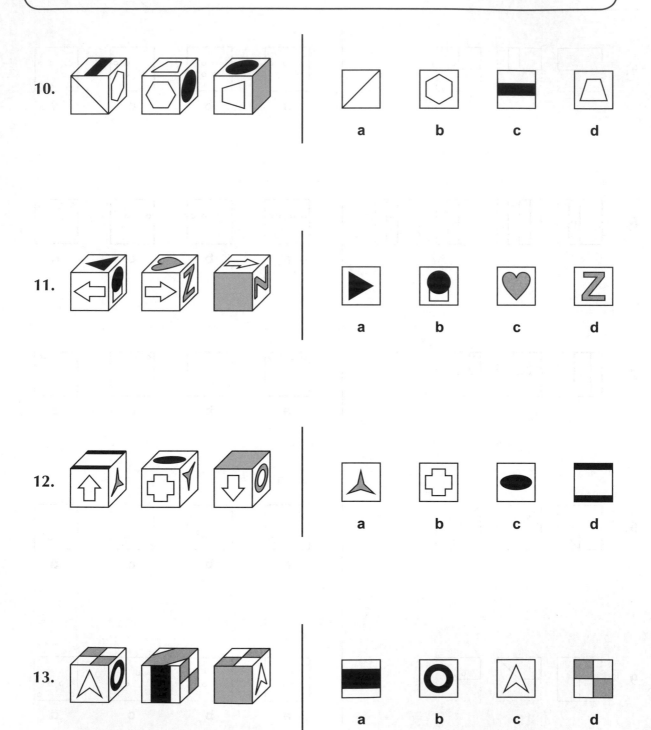

10.

a   b   c   d

11.

a   b   c   d

12.

a   b   c   d

13.

a   b   c   d

Work out which set of blocks can be put together to make the 3D figure on the left.

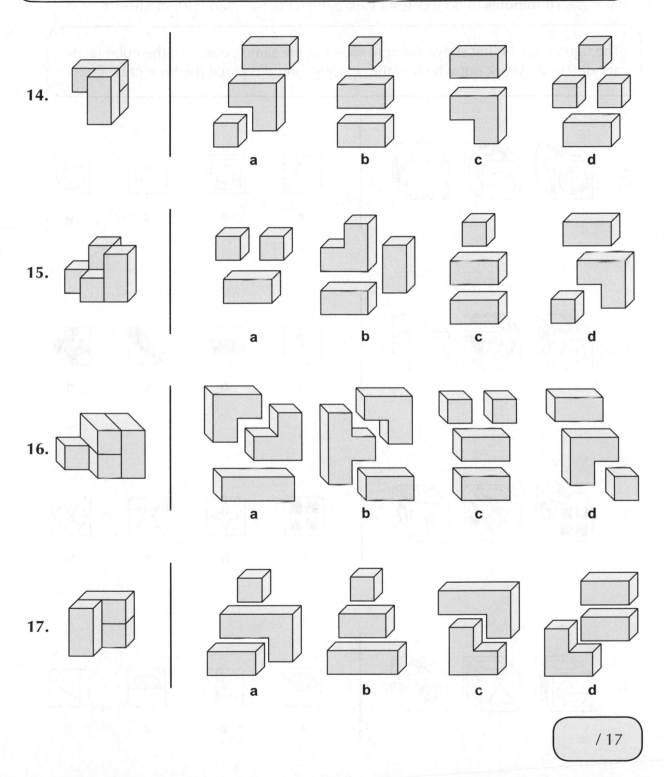

14.

a   b   c   d

15.

a   b   c   d

16.

a   b   c   d

17.

a   b   c   d

/ 17

You have **10 minutes** to do this test. Circle the letter for each correct answer.

The figures on the left show different views of the same cube. All the cube faces are different. Work out which of the options should replace the blue cube face.

1.

                                                 a   **b**   **c**   **d**

2.

                                                 a   **b**   **c**   **d**

3.

                                                 a   **b**   **c**   **d**

4.

                                                 a   **b**   **c**   **d**

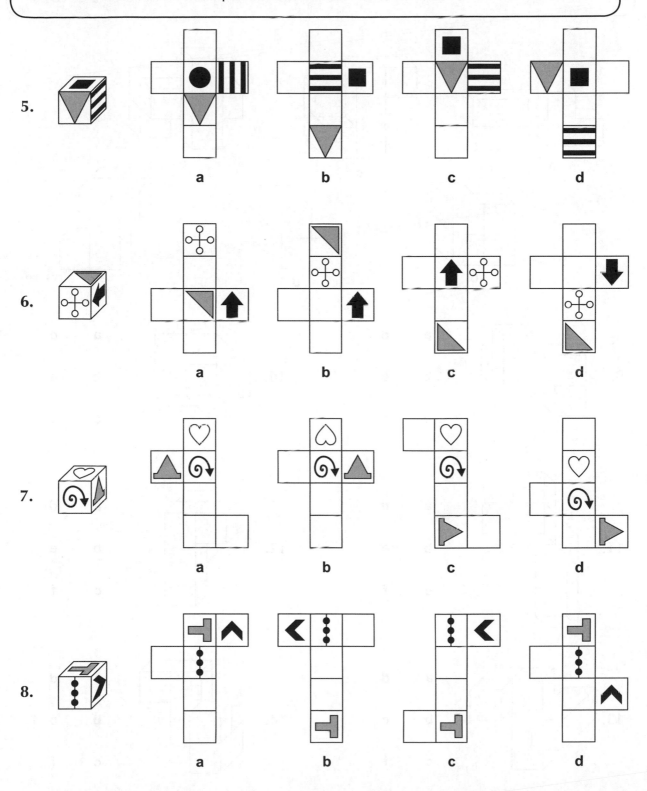

5.

a   b   c   d

6.

a   b   c   d

7.

a   b   c   d

8.

a   b   c   d

Test 20

Work out which 3D figure in the grey box has been rotated to make the new 3D figure.

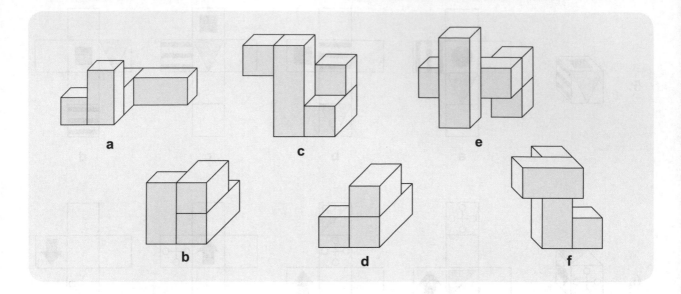

a

c

e

b

d

f

9.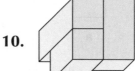

a	d
b	e
c	f

10.

a	d
b	e
c	f

11.

a	d
b	e
c	f

12.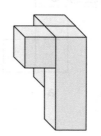

a	d
b	e
c	f

13.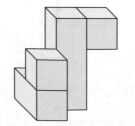

a	d
b	e
c	f

14.

a	d
b	e
c	f

92

Without rotating the figure on the left, work out which option fits onto it to make the 3D shape in the grey box.

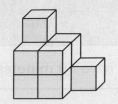

15.

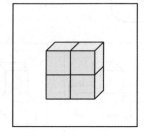

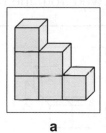   a

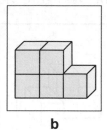   b

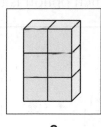   c

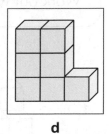   d

16.

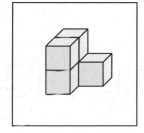

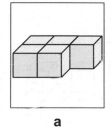   a

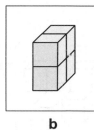   b

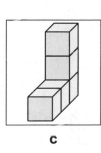   c

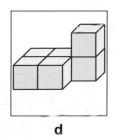   d

17.

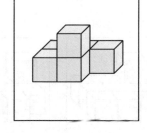

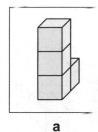   a

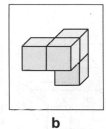   b

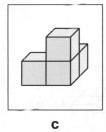   c

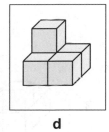   d

18.

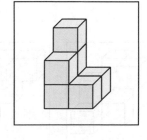

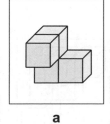   a

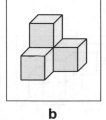   b

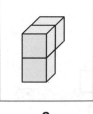   c

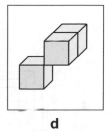   d

/ 18

93

You have **10 minutes** to do this test. Circle the letter for each correct answer.

Work out which option is the 3D figure viewed from the **right**.

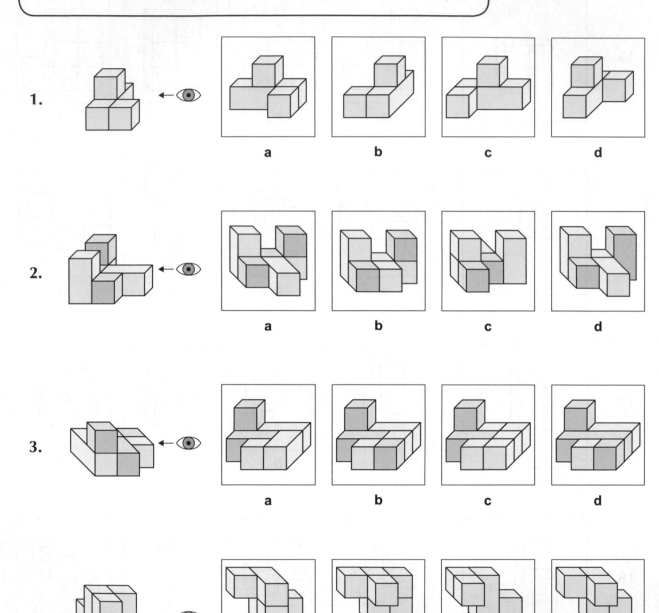

1.

a   b   c   d

2.

a   b   c   d

3.

a   b   c   d

4.

a   b   c   d

94

Work out which option shows the figure on the left when folded along the dotted line.

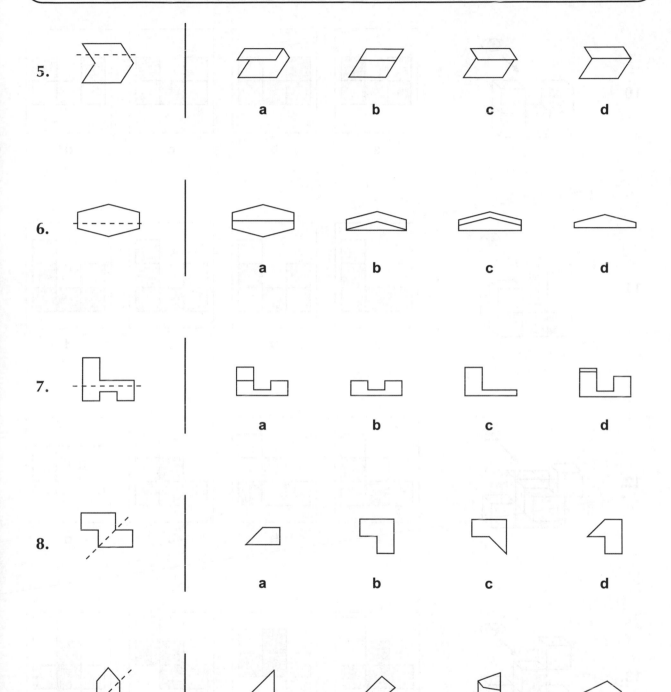

5.

        a   b   c   d

6.

        a   b   c   d

7.

        a   b   c   d

8.

        a   b   c   d

9.

        a   b   c   d

Test 21

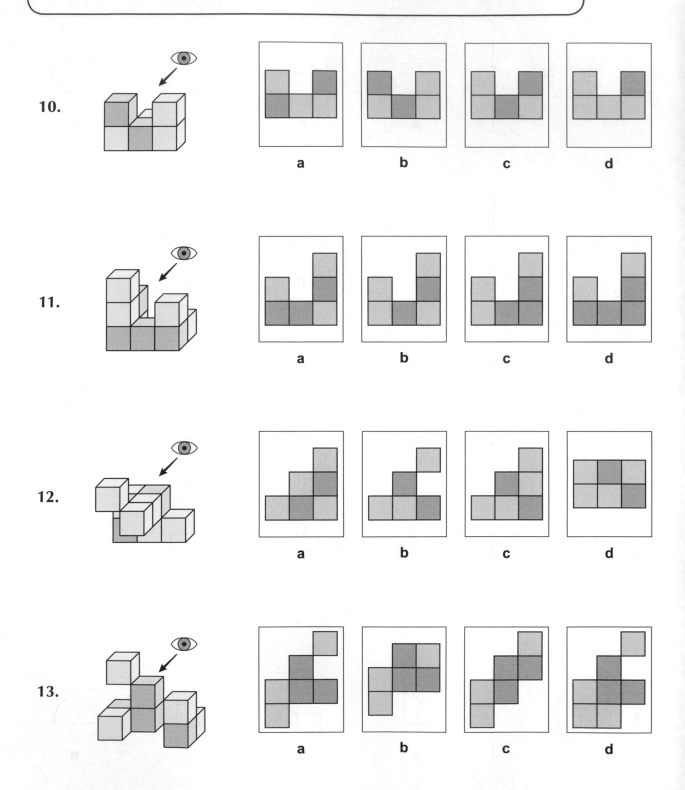

10.

a   b   c   d

11.

a   b   c   d

12.

a   b   c   d

13.

a   b   c   d

Work out which of the four cubes can be made from the net.

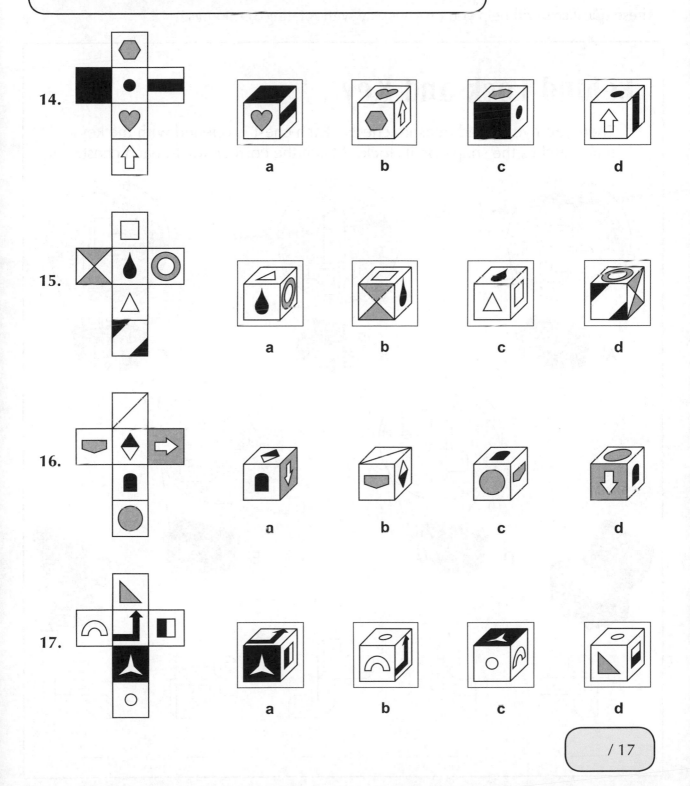

14.

a   b   c   d

15.

a   b   c   d

16.

a   b   c   d

17.

a   b   c   d

/ 17

97

Test 21

These questions will help you on your way with **rotating 3D shapes**.

Behind Lock and Key

There are five locked treasure chests. Each chest is opened with the key that matches the shape on its lock. Match the correct key to each chest.

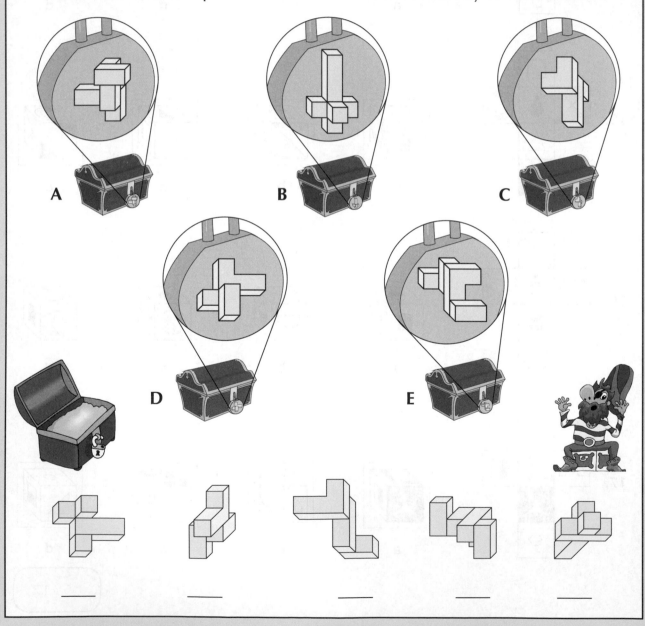

A

B

C

D

E

___   ___   ___   ___   ___

You have **10 minutes** to do this test. Circle the letter for each correct answer.

Work out which option is a 2D view from **above** the 3D figure shown.

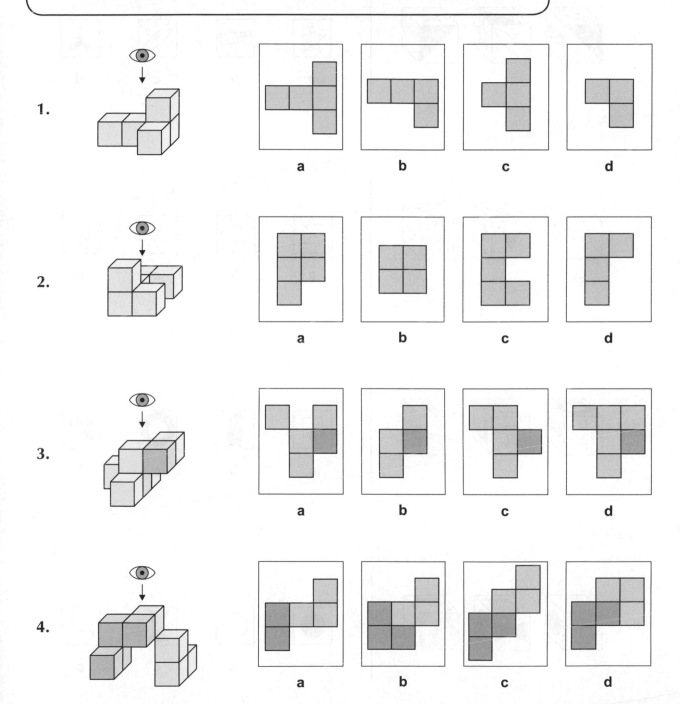

1.

a   b   c   d

2.

a   b   c   d

3.

a   b   c   d

4.

a   b   c   d

99

The figures on the left show different views of the same cube. All the cube faces are different. Work out which of the options should replace the blue cube face.

5.

| a | b | c | d |

6.

| a | b | c | d |

7.

| a | b | c | d |

8.

| a | b | c | d |

100

Work out which 3D figure in the grey box has been rotated to make the new 3D figure.

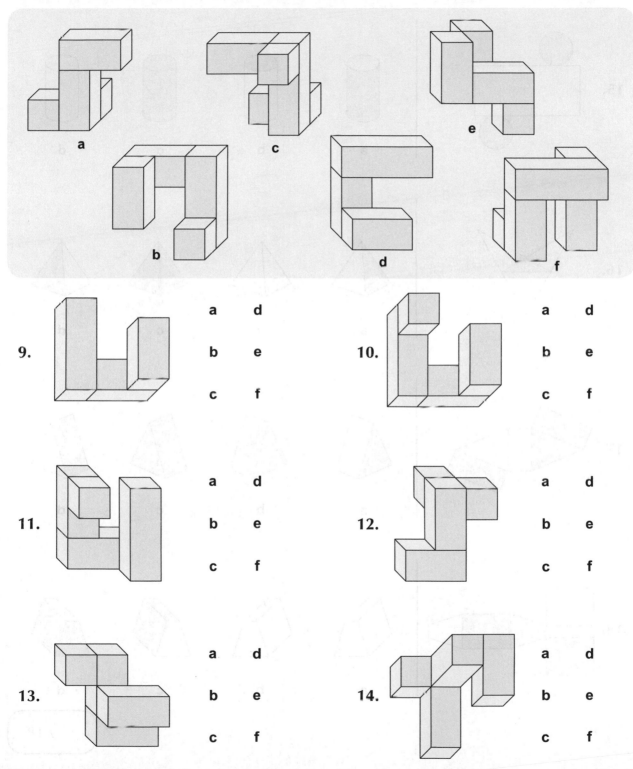

9.　　　a　　d
　　　　b　　e
　　　　c　　f

10.　　a　　d
　　　　b　　e
　　　　c　　f

11.　　a　　d
　　　　b　　e
　　　　c　　f

12.　　a　　d
　　　　b　　e
　　　　c　　f

13.　　a　　d
　　　　b　　e
　　　　c　　f

14.　　a　　d
　　　　b　　e
　　　　c　　f

Work out which of the 3D shapes can be made from the net.

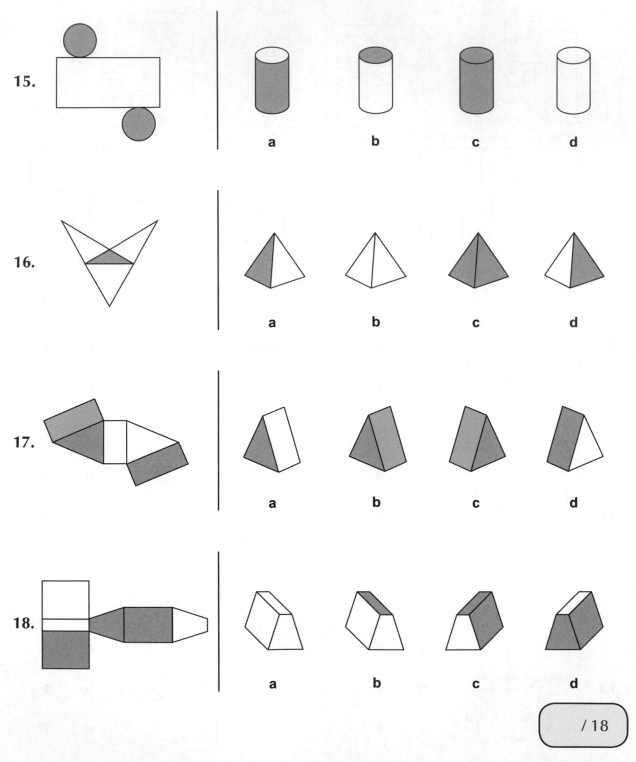

15.

a   b   c   d

16.

a   b   c   d

17.

a   b   c   d

18.

a   b   c   d

/ 18

You have **10 minutes** to do this test. Circle the letter for each correct answer.

A square is folded and then a hole is punched, as shown on the left. Work out which option shows the square when unfolded.

1.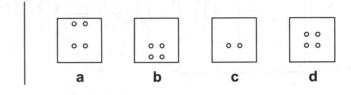

a　　b　　c　　d

2.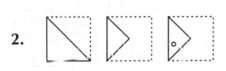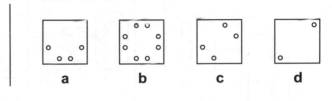

a　　b　　c　　d

3.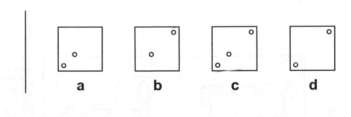

a　　b　　c　　d

4.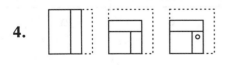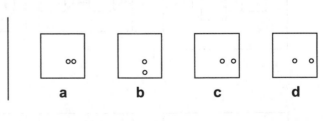

a　　b　　c　　d

5.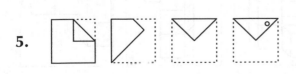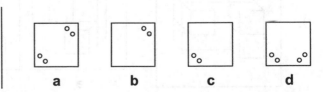

a　　b　　c　　d

Without rotating the figure on the left, work out which option fits onto it to make the 3D shape in the grey box.

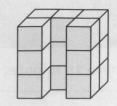

6. 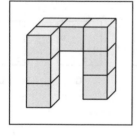   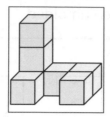 **a**   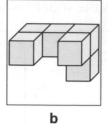 **b**   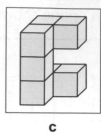 **c**   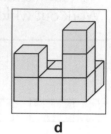 **d**

7. 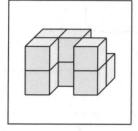   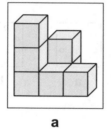 **a**   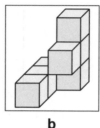 **b**   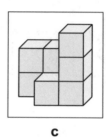 **c**   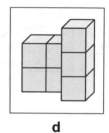 **d**

8. 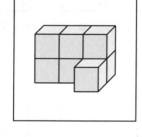   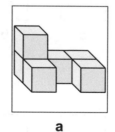 **a**   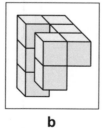 **b**   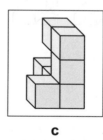 **c**   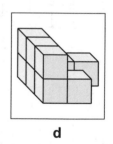 **d**

9. 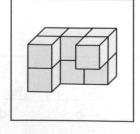   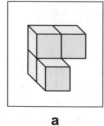 **a**   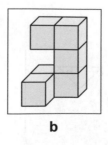 **b**   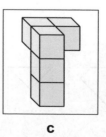 **c**   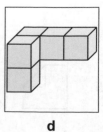 **d**

Work out which option is the 3D figure viewed from the **left**.

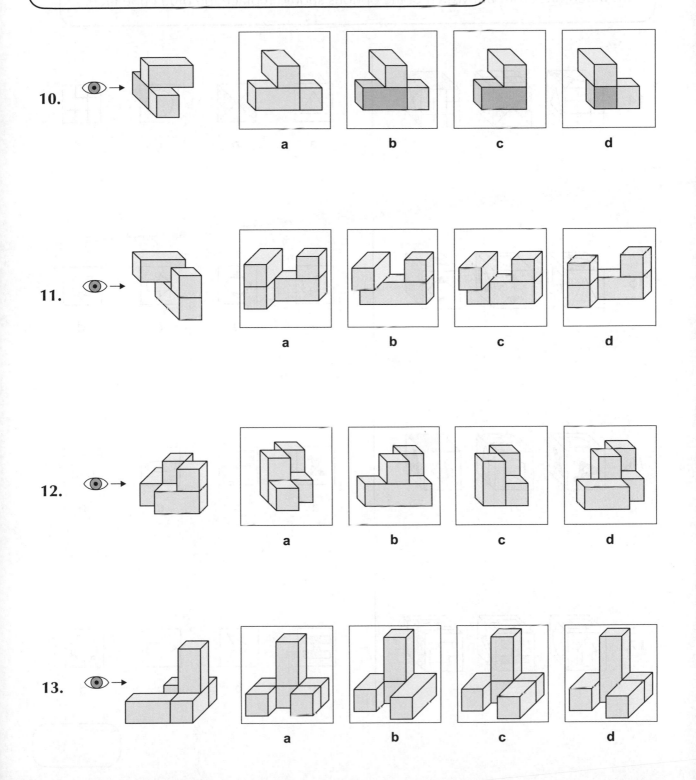

10.

a b c d

11.

a b c d

12.

a b c d

13.

a b c d

Test 23

The figures on the left show different views of the same cube. All the cube faces are different. Work out which of the options should replace the blue cube face.

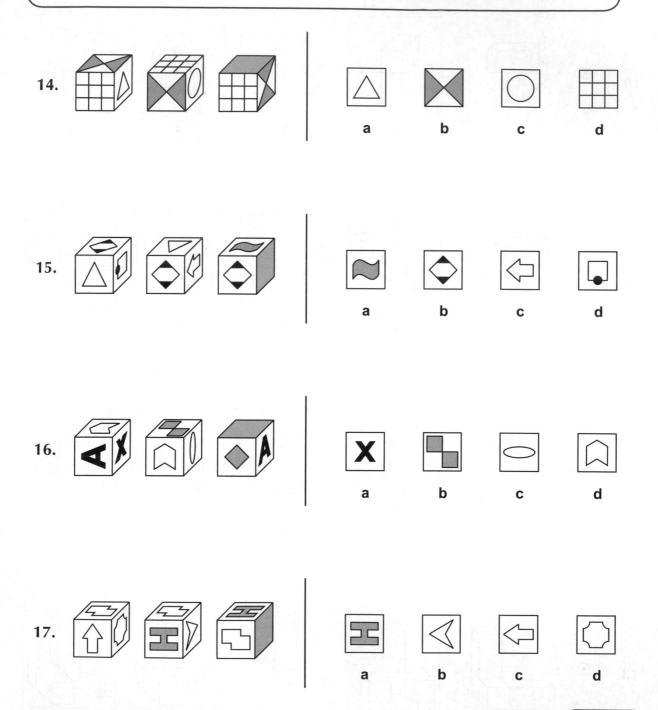

14.

a   b   c   d

15.

a   b   c   d

16.

a   b   c   d

17.

a   b   c   d

/ 17

Test 24

You have **10 minutes** to do this test. Circle the letter for each correct answer.

Work out which option shows the figure on the left when folded along the dotted line.

1.

    a   b   c   d

2.

    a   b   c   d

3.

    a   b   c   d

4.

    a   b   c   d

5.

    a   b   c   d

Test 24

Work out which set of blocks can be put together to make the 3D figure on the left.

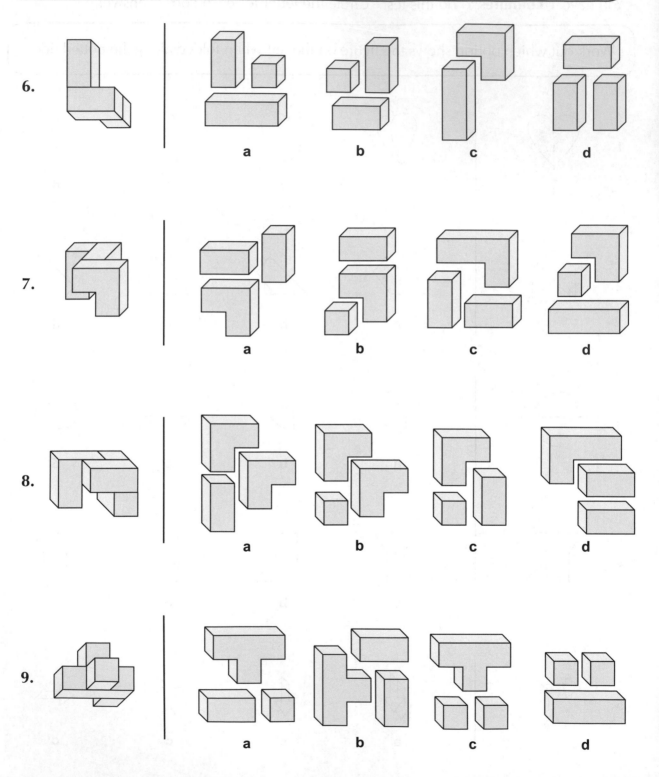

6.

a   b   c   d

7.

a   b   c   d

8.

a   b   c   d

9.

a   b   c   d

Work out which of the four cubes can be made from the net.

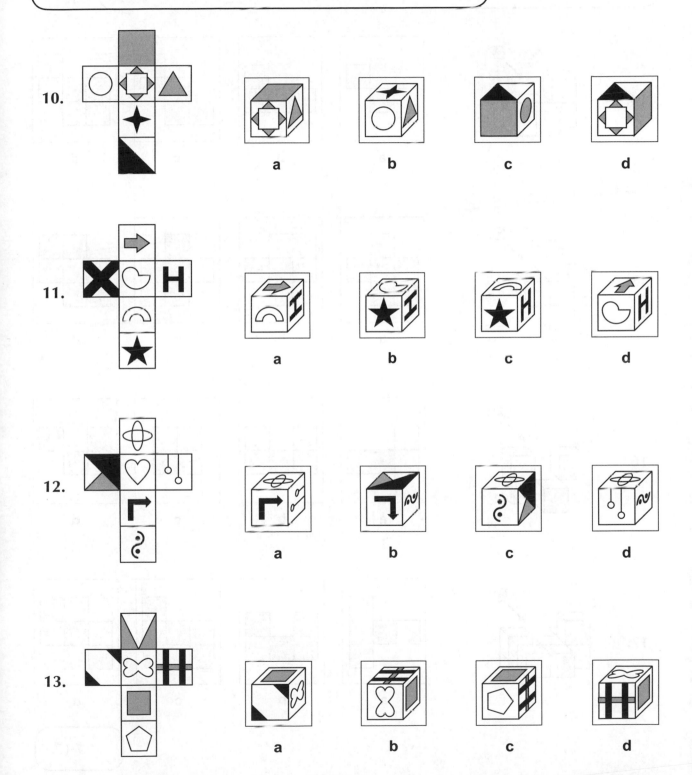

10.

a   b   c   d

11.

a   b   c   d

12.

a   b   c   d

13.

a   b   c   d

Test 24

Work out which option is a 2D view from the **back** of the 3D figure shown.

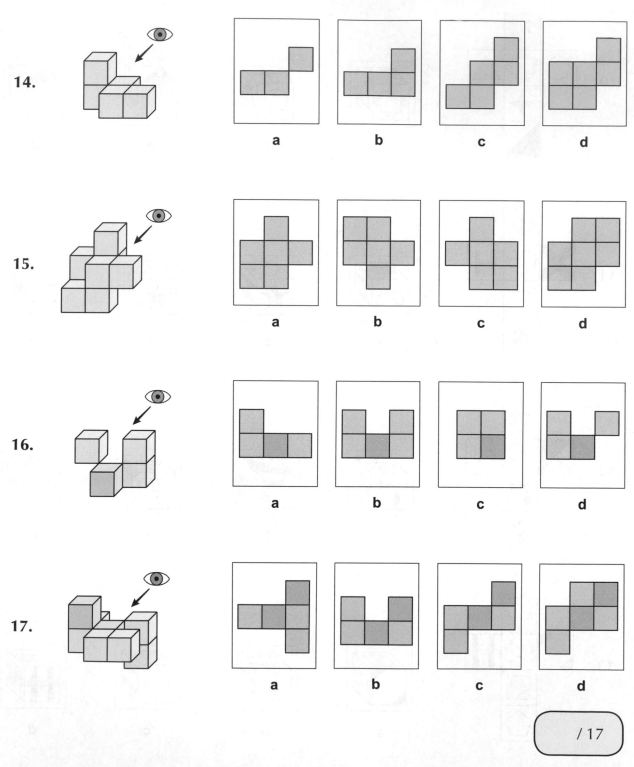

14.

   a   b   c   d

15.

   a   b   c   d

16.

   a   b   c   d

17.

   a   b   c   d

/ 17

Puzzles 8

This feels like the perfect time to practise your **complete the shape** and **net** skills.

Castle Calamity

Centuries ago, Cuboid Castle was damaged in the legendary Battle of the Blocks. From the options below, choose the shape that would best repair the damage.

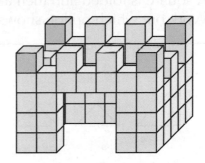

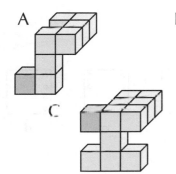

A

B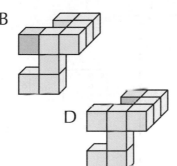

C

D

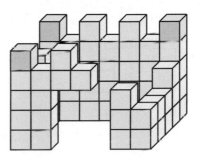

Clowning Around

The clown in Ellie's jack-in-the-box pops out the top of the box shown in the picture on the right. Using the net, choose the option below which shows another way Ellie can hold the box so that the clown pops out.

A

B

C

D

You have **10 minutes** to do this test. Circle the letter for each correct answer.

> A square is folded and then a hole is punched, as shown on the left.
> Work out which option shows the square when unfolded.

1.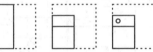

   a   **b**   **c**   **d**

2.

   a   **b**   **c**   **d**

3.

   a   **b**   **c**   **d**

4.

   a   **b**   **c**   **d**

5.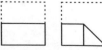

   a   **b**   **c**   **d**

Work out which set of blocks can be put together to make the 3D figure on the left.

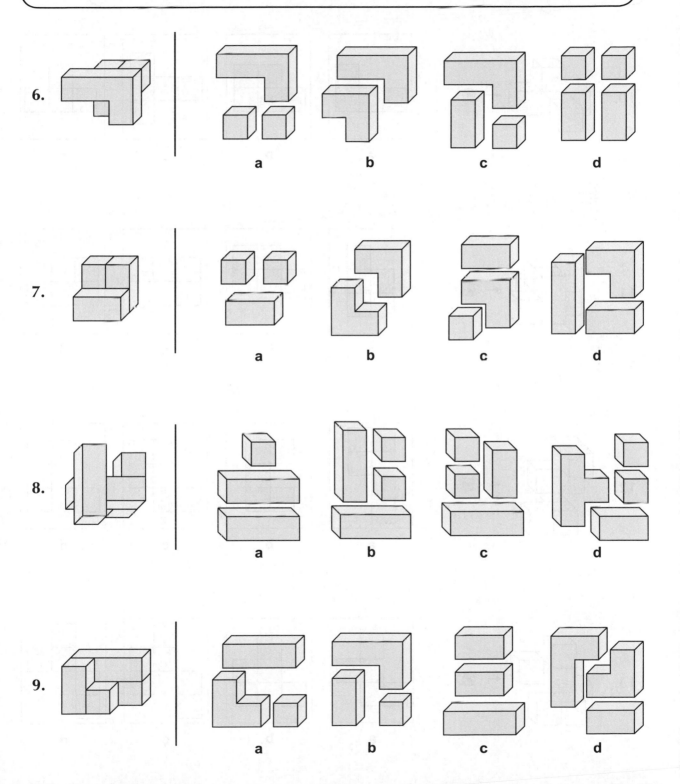

6.

a   b   c   d

7.

a   b   c   d

8.

a   b   c   d

9.

a   b   c   d

Test 25

Work out which option is a 2D view from the **right** of the 3D figure shown.

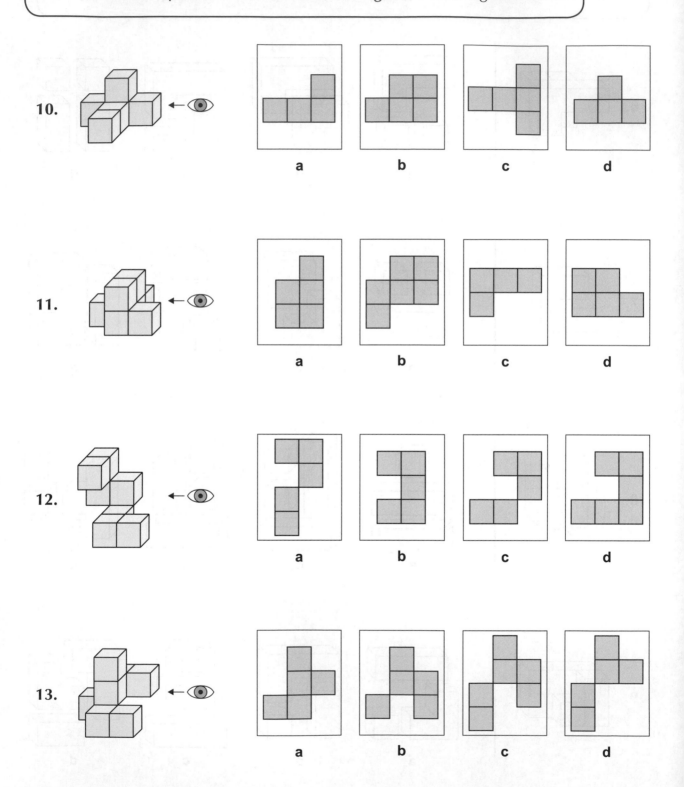

10.

    a   b   c   d

11.

    a   b   c   d

12.

    a   b   c   d

13.

    a   b   c   d

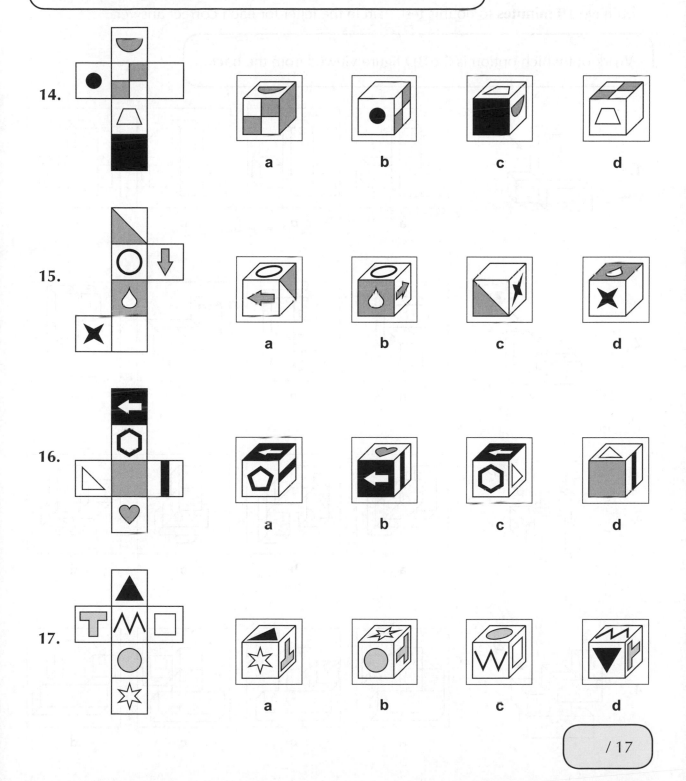

14.

a b c d

15.

a b c d

16.

a b c d

17.

a b c d

/ 17

115

You have **10 minutes** to do this test. Circle the letter for each correct answer.

Work out which option is the 3D figure viewed from the **back**.

1.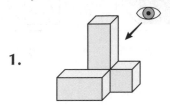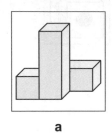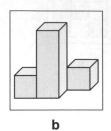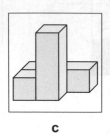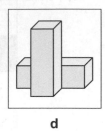

a   b   c   d

2.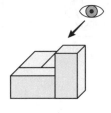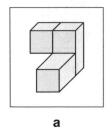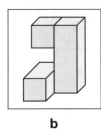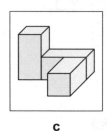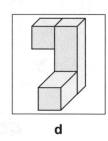

a   b   c   d

3.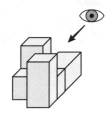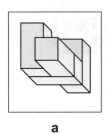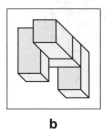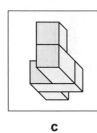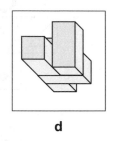

a   b   c   d

4.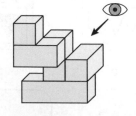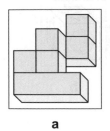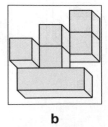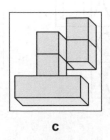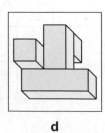

a   b   c   d

Work out which of the four partial nets can be folded to make the cube on the left.

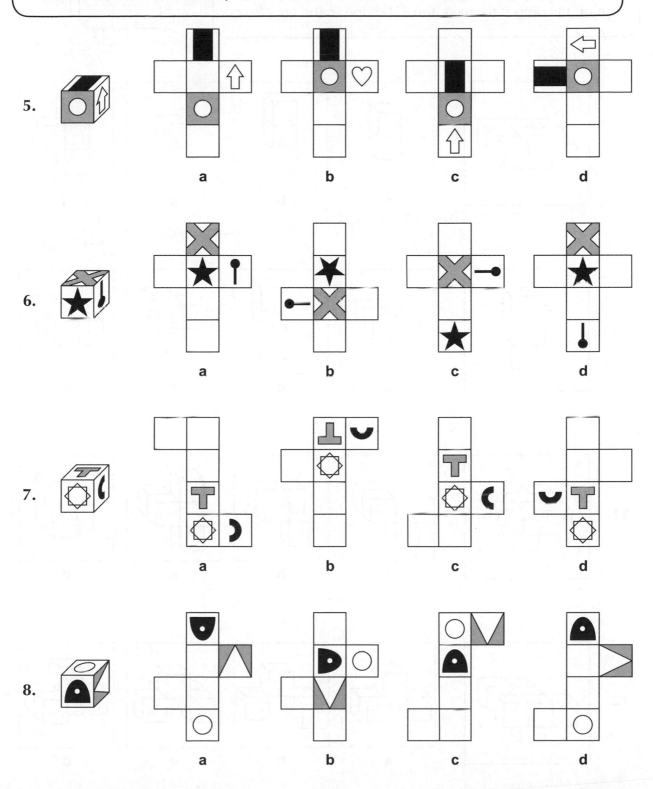

5.

a   b   c   d

6.

a   b   c   d

7.

a   b   c   d

8.

a   b   c   d

Test 26

Without rotating the figure on the left, work out which option fits onto it to make the 3D shape in the grey box.

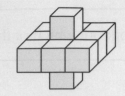

9.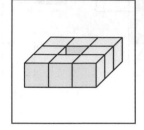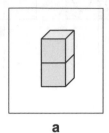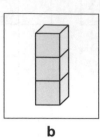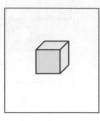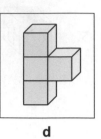

         a   b   c   d

10.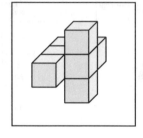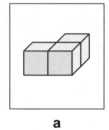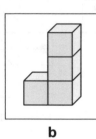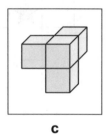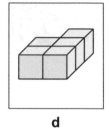

         a   b   c   d

11.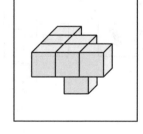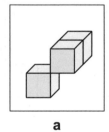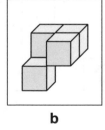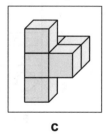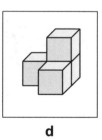

         a   b   c   d

12.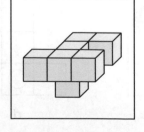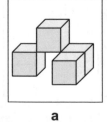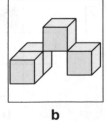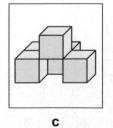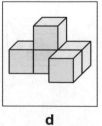

         a   b   c   d

A square is folded and then a hole is punched, as shown on the left.
Work out which option shows the square when unfolded.

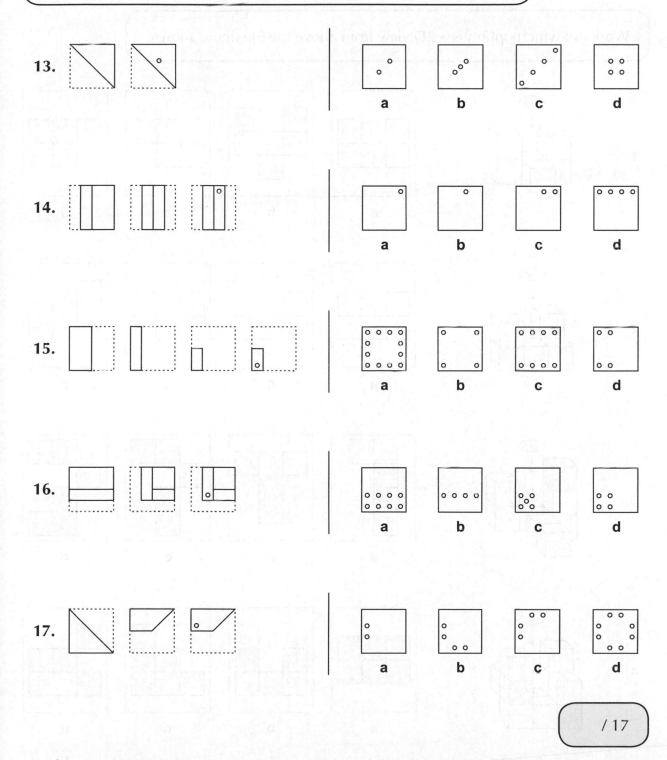

13.

a b c d

14.

a b c d

15.

a b c d

16.

a b c d

17.

a b c d

/ 17

Test 26

You have **10 minutes** to do this test. Circle the letter for each correct answer.

Work out which option is a 2D view from **above** the 3D figure shown.

1.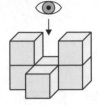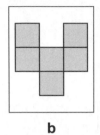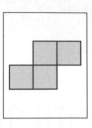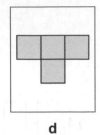

                                  a   **b**   **c**   **d**

2.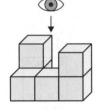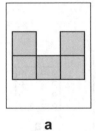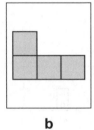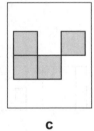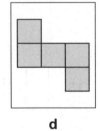

                                  a   **b**   **c**   **d**

3.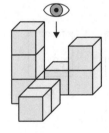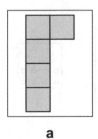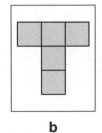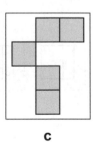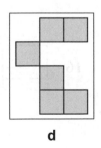

                                  a   **b**   **c**   **d**

4.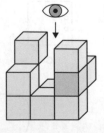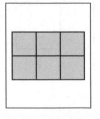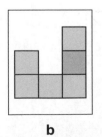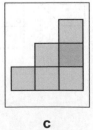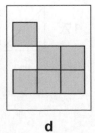

                                  a   **b**   **c**   **d**

120

Work out which of the 3D shapes can be made from the net.

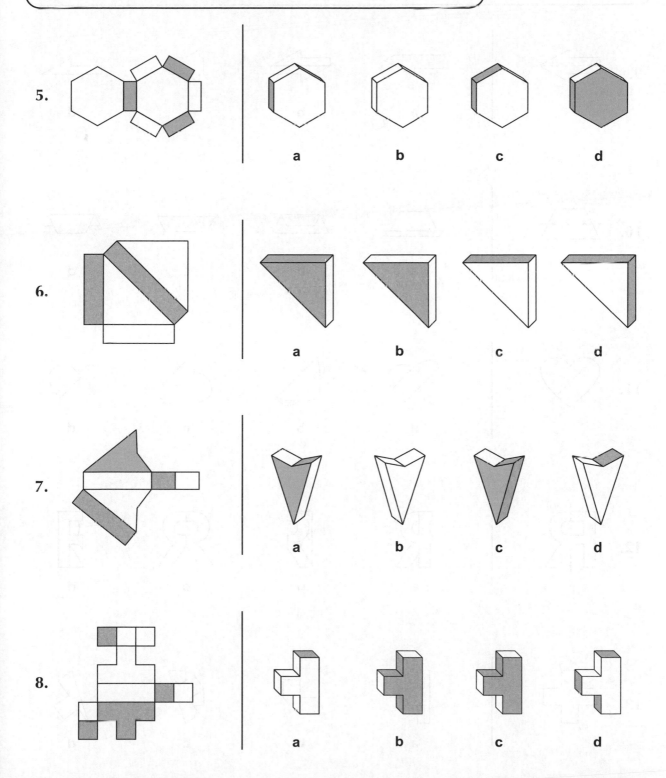

5.

a   b   c   d

6.

a   b   c   d

7.

a   b   c   d

8.

a   b   c   d

121

Work out which option shows the figure on the left when folded along the dotted line.

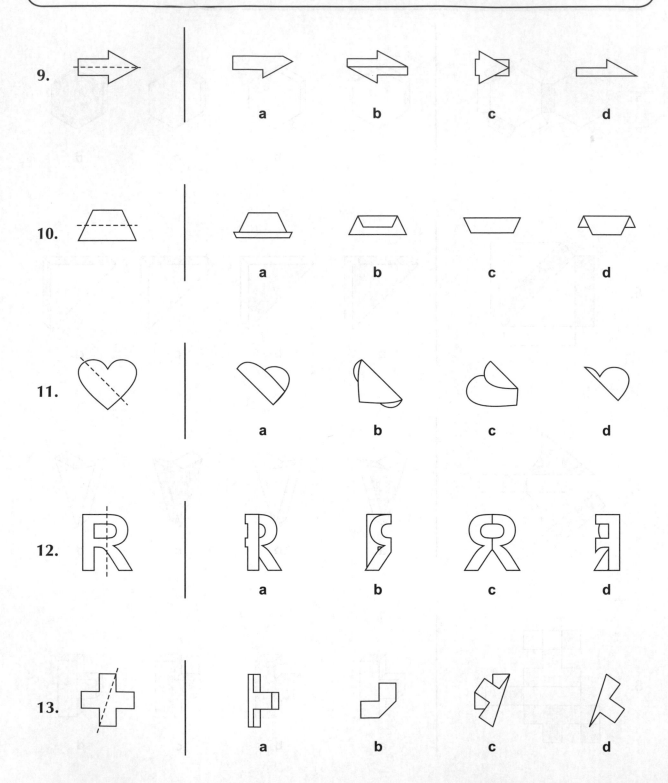

9.

        a   b   c   d

10.

        a   b   c   d

11.

        a   b   c   d

12.

        a   b   c   d

13.

        a   b   c   d

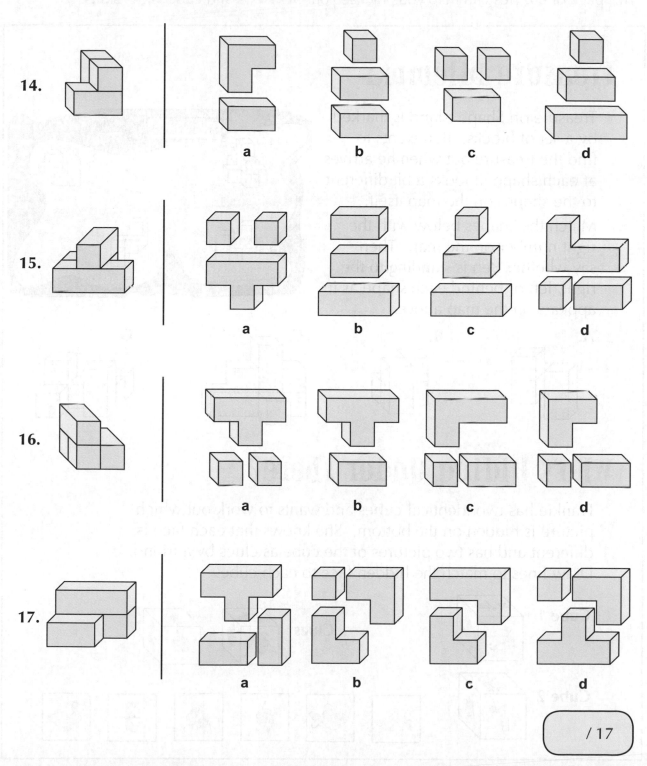

14.

a   b   c   d

15.

a   b   c   d

16.

a   b   c   d

17.

a   b   c   d

/ 17

This page of puzzles will help you practise your **3D views** and **cube views** skills.

Treasure Dilemma

Treasure on Shape Island is marked by a set of blocks. Ben wants to find the treasure but when he arrives at each shape, it looks a bit different to the shapes on the map itself.

Match the shapes below with the right number on the map. Then say whether Ben is standing to the right, left or behind each shape as it appears on the map above.

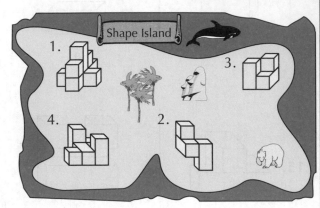

A.

B.

C.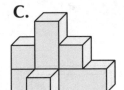

D.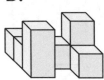

Who's Hiding Under There?

Frankie has two identical cubes and wants to work out which picture is hidden on the bottom. She knows that each face is different and has two pictures of the cube as clues by a friend. Draw lines to match the hidden face to each cube.

Cube 1

Clues

Cube 2

⏱ 10

You have **10 minutes** to do this test. Circle the letter for each correct answer.

Work out which option is a 2D view from the **left** of the 3D figure shown.

1.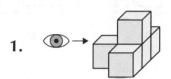

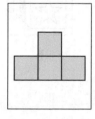 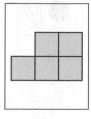 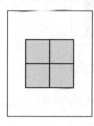 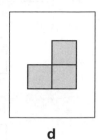

  a   b   c   d

2.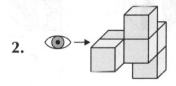

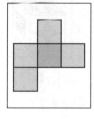 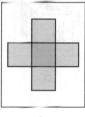 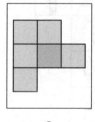 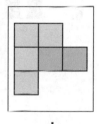

  a   b   c   d

3.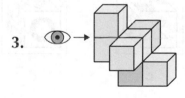

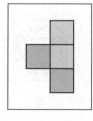 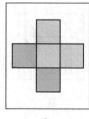 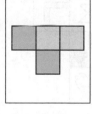 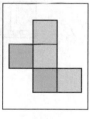

  a   b   c   d

4.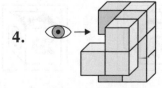

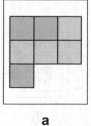 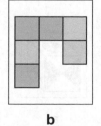 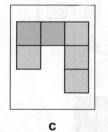 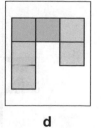

  a   b   c   d

Work out which of the four cubes can be made from the net.

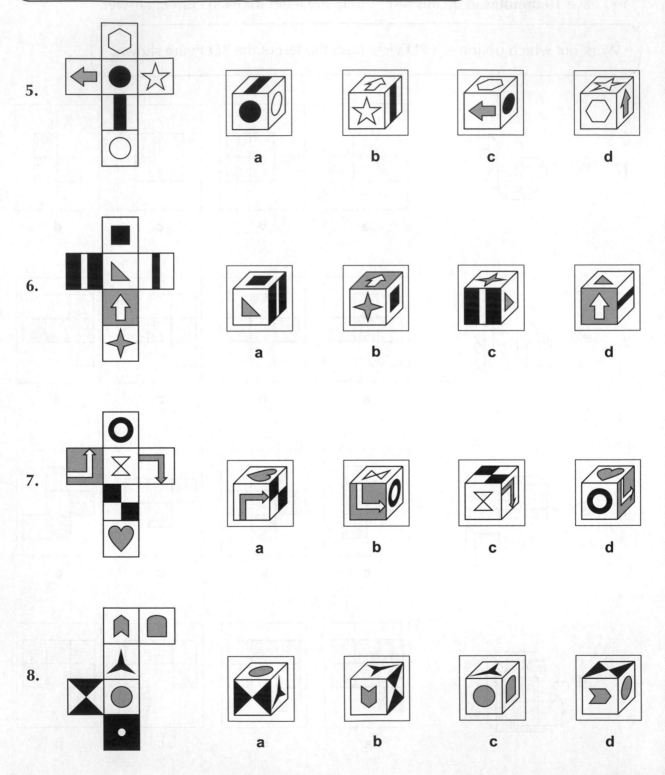

5. a   b   c   d

6. a   b   c   d

7. a   b   c   d

8. a   b   c   d

Without rotating the figure on the left, work out which
option fits onto it to make the 3D shape in the grey box.

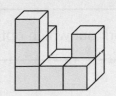

9.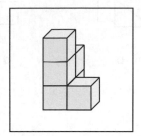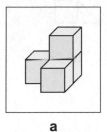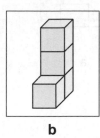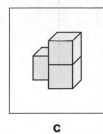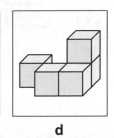

                                a   b   c   d

10.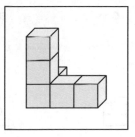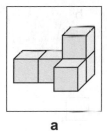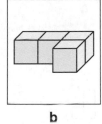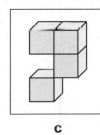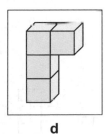

                                a   b   c   d

11.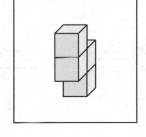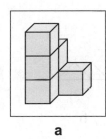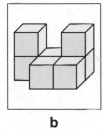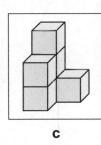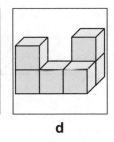

                                a   b   c   d

12.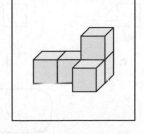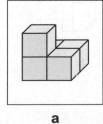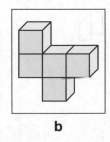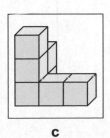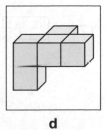

                                a   b   c   d

13.

    a   b   c   d

14.

    a   b   c   d

15.

    a   b   c   d

16.

    a   b   c   d

17.

    a   b   c   d

/ 17

You have **10 minutes** to do this test. Circle the letter for each correct answer.

Work out which set of blocks can be put together to make the 3D figure on the left.

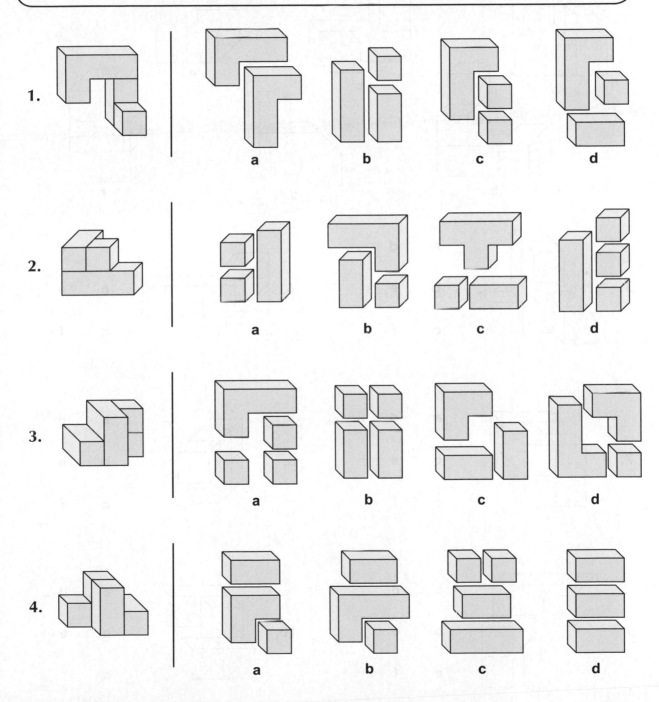

1.

a   b   c   d

2.

a   b   c   d

3.

a   b   c   d

4.

a   b   c   d

Work out which 3D figure in the grey box has been rotated to make the new 3D figure.

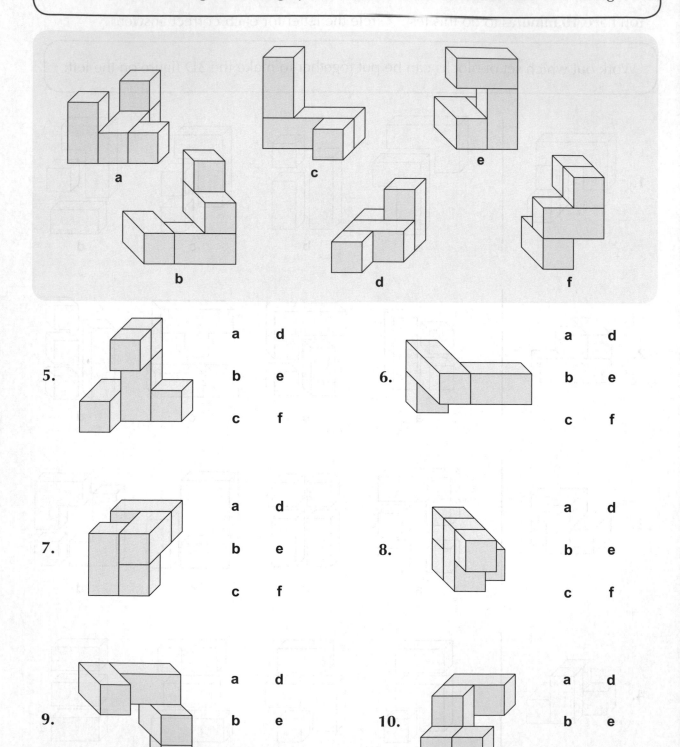

5.

a	d
b	e
c	f

6.

a	d
b	e
c	f

7.

a	d
b	e
c	f

8.

a	d
b	e
c	f

9.

a	d
b	e
c	f

10.

a	d
b	e
c	f

130

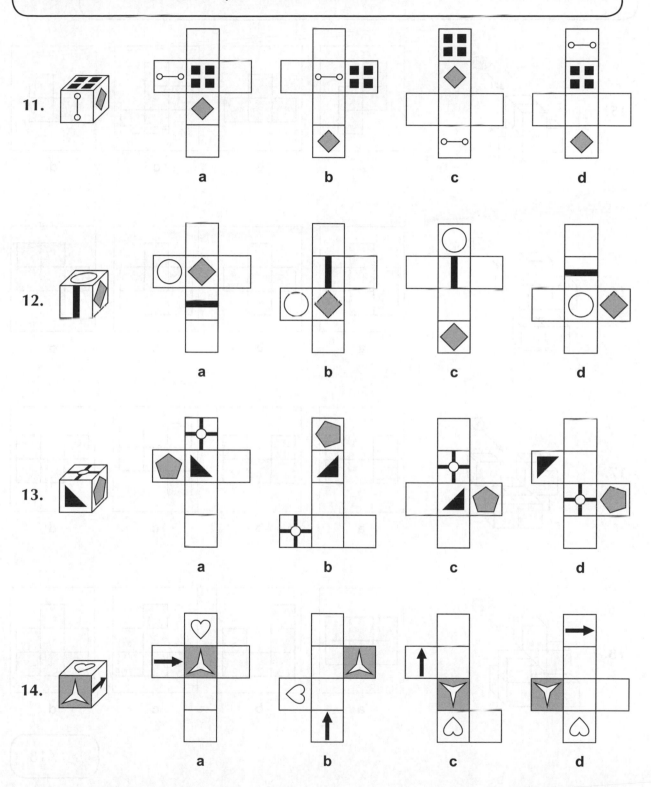

11.

a   b   c   d

12.

a   b   c   d

13.

a   b   c   d

14.

a   b   c   d

131

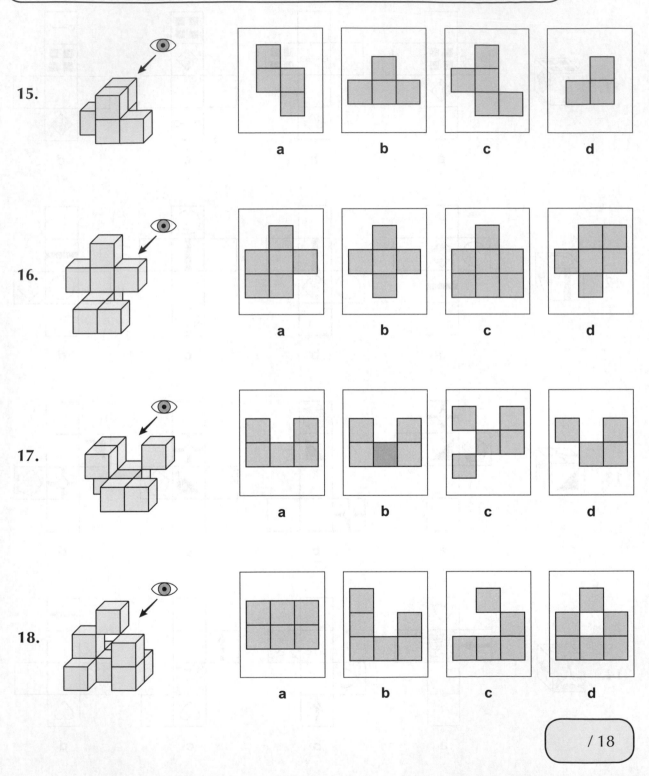

15.

a   b   c   d

16.

a   b   c   d

17.

a   b   c   d

18.

a   b   c   d

/ 18

Test 30

You have **10 minutes** to do this test. Circle the letter for each correct answer.

Work out which 3D figure in the grey box has been rotated to make the new 3D figure.

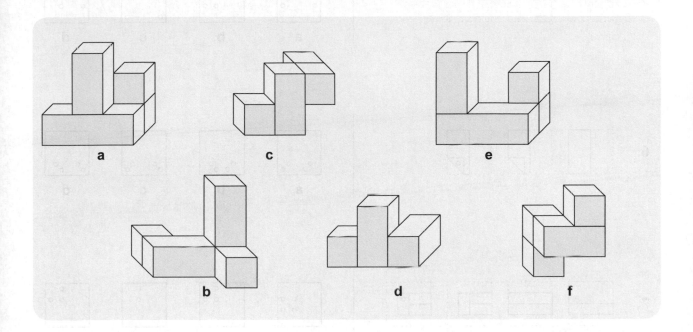

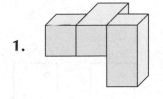

1.

a	d
b	e
c	f

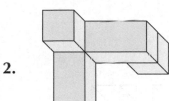

2.

a	d
b	e
c	f

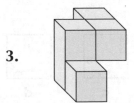

3.

a	d
b	e
c	f

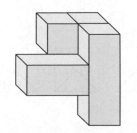

4.

a	d
b	e
c	f

A square is folded and then a hole is punched, as shown on the left.
Work out which option shows the square when unfolded.

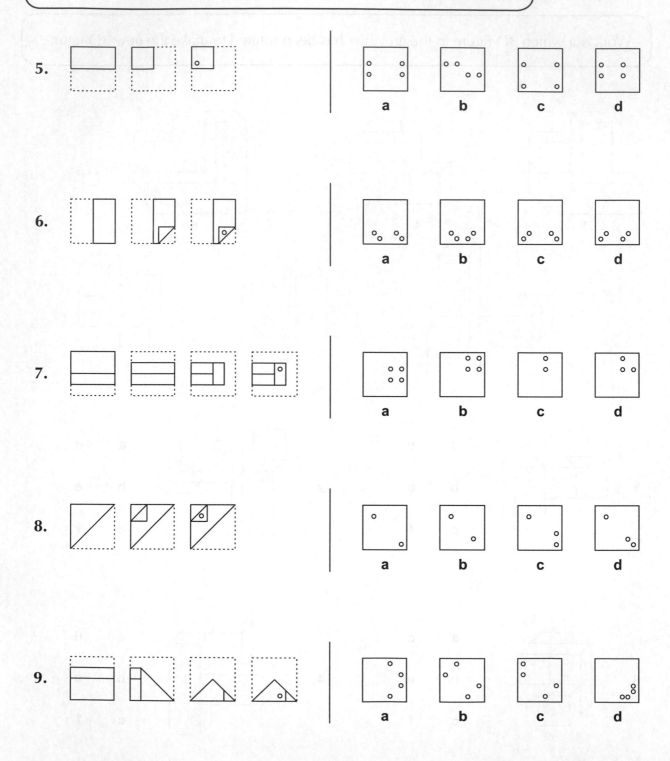

5. | a b c d

6. | a b c d

7. | a b c d

8. | a b c d

9. | a b c d

Work out which of the 3D shapes can be made from the net.

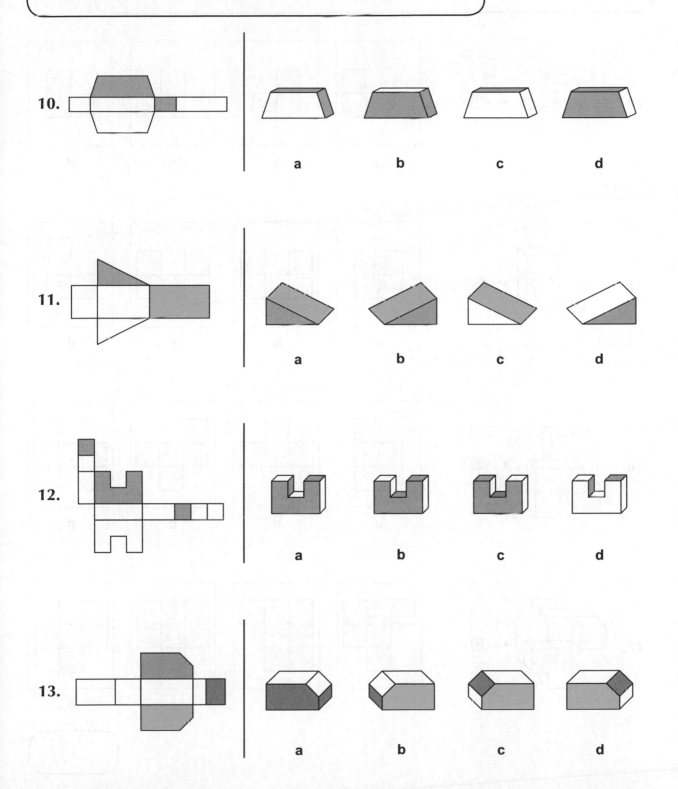

10.
a   b   c   d

11.
a   b   c   d

12.
a   b   c   d

13.
a   b   c   d

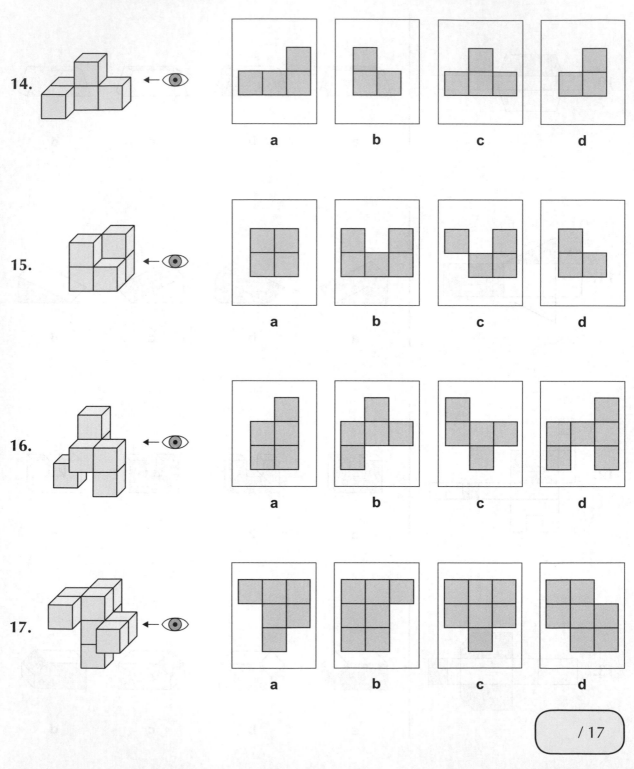

14.

a   b   c   d

15.

a   b   c   d

16.

a   b   c   d

17.

a   b   c   d

/ 17

You have **10 minutes** to do this test. Circle the letter for each correct answer.

Work out which option shows the figure on the left when folded along the dotted line.

1.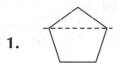

a   b   c   d

2.

a   b   c   d

3.

a   b   c   d

4.

a   b   c   d

5.

a   b   c   d

Work out which option is a 2D view from **above** the 3D figure shown.

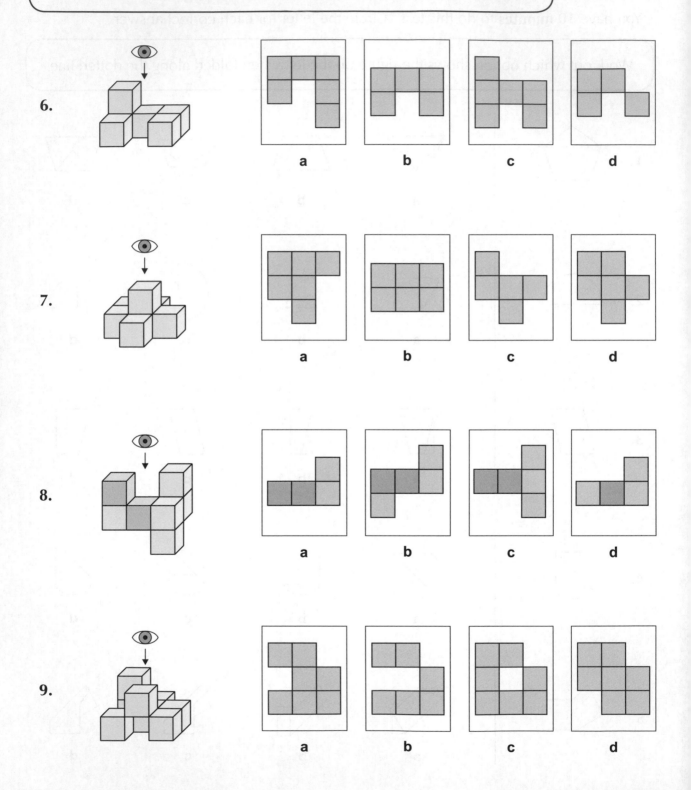

6.
a
b
c
d

7.
a
b
c
d

8.
a
b
c
d

9.
a
b
c
d

138

Work out which of the four cubes can be made from the net.

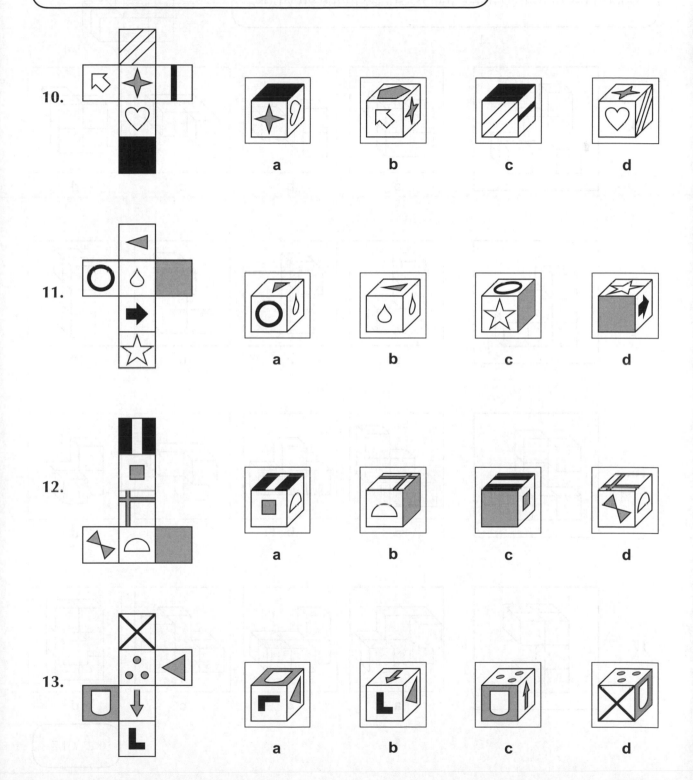

10.

a   b   c   d

11.

a   b   c   d

12.

a   b   c   d

13.

a   b   c   d

Test 31

Without rotating the figure on the left, work out which option fits onto it to make the 3D shape in the grey box.

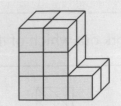

14.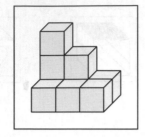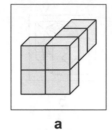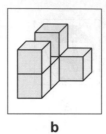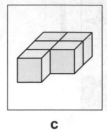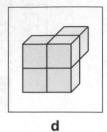

a   b   c   d

15.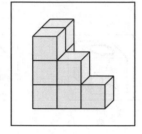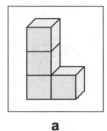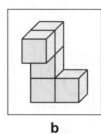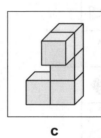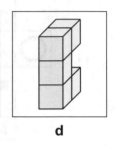

a   b   c   d

16.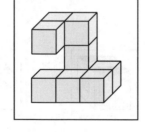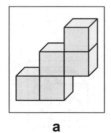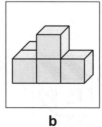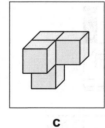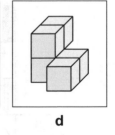

a   b   c   d

17.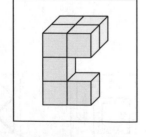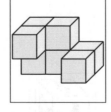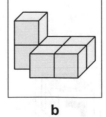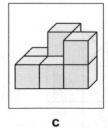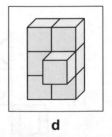

a   b   c   d

Try these puzzles — they're a great way to practise **2D views** and **folding** and **punching**.

Bursting Birthday Balloons

Archie the archer received 9 cube-shaped presents for his birthday. Each one has a balloon attached directly above it.

Archie bursts all the balloons by carefully choosing where he shoots from.

What is the minimum number of arrows Archie needs to shoot in order to burst all the balloons?

The Hole Truth

The holes in the shapes below have been made by punching a single hole through each shape while it was folded up.

Can you work out how each shape was folded?

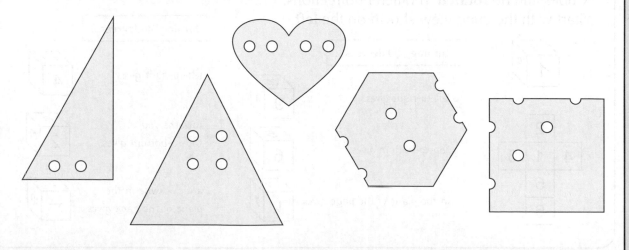

Glossary

Folding Nets

Nets should be folded **into the page**.

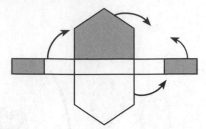

Fold the faces away from you until they all come together.

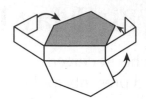

This shape can now be rotated.

3D Rotation

There are **three planes** that a 3D shape can be rotated in.

1. 90 degrees towards you, top-to-bottom

90 degrees away from you, top-to-bottom

2.

90 degrees left-to-right

90 degrees right-to-left

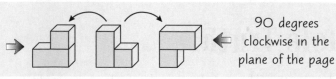

3. 90 degrees anticlockwise in the plane of the page

90 degrees clockwise in the plane of the page

Cubes and Nets

Cubes can be **rotated** in different directions.
Start with the cube view shown on the **left**.

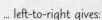

	2	
4	1	3
	5	
	6	

Turning 180 degrees...

... left-to-right gives:

... top-to-bottom gives:

... in the plane of the page gives:

Turning 90 degrees...

... left-to-right gives:

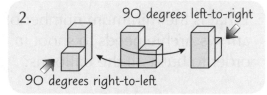

... towards you, top-to-bottom gives:

... anticlockwise in the plane of the page gives:

NDXPDE2